Monica Carr's COUNTRY DIARY

Published by Cork Publishing Limited
19 Rutland Street, Cork
for
The Farming Independent
Independent Newspapers
90 Middle Abbey Street, Dublin 1.

Articles selected and compiled by Eamonn Holmes,
Paddy Smith and Michael Hegarty.
Edited by Mairéad McGuinness.
Illustrations by Phelim Connolly.

A catalogue record of this book is available from the
British Library.

ISBN 1-86076-955-1

Printed in Ireland by Colour Books.

CONTENTS

MONICA CARR

Meeting Monica Carr was, for me, a revelation.

Here I was, new into the world of agricultural journalism, being introduced to a woman with an immense personality.

I remember being astonished to learn that Monica Carr was not real. That is to say, Monica was not her real name. The Monica Carr of my childhood and early years was, I learned, Mary Norton. That was the first revelation.

Next, I was to learn that Monica's entire family of husband, children and extended in-laws and out-laws existed only in the fertile, devilish mind of Mary Norton. But, for myself and countless readers of her very popular "Country Diary" in the *Farming Independent*, Monica Carr was very much a real live country-woman, family and all – open fires, home-cooking and haymaking thrown in.

In truth, readers like myself would not have been surprised to learn that it was the Mary Norton persona which was the invented one, as we revelled in her stories of summer bliss on the Shannon, listening for song birds, Christmas in the country and countless other tales of country life.

In her "diary", Monica Carr has captured the atmosphere of another era, a slower one, perhaps an idyllic one. She has warmed the hearts of those who delve in each week, with her tales about a day at the mart with husband Tom, or about the antics of the noisy inhabitants of the rookery close to the farmyard.

Her grandmother Carr's recipes (for everything from a cure for chilblains to the most delicious plum jam) have been very popular features of her weekly column.

Monica is the respectable mother, minding her clutch but finding it increasingly hard to understand some of the attitudes of modern youth. Gentle, almost genteel, and a tireless campaigner for the values of yesteryear.

Mary, on the other hand, is a single woman – and singular in her outlook, surprisingly open-minded and liberal for a woman of her generation. She has a wicked sense of humour – and a sharp tongue, if she senses even a whiff of hypocrisy.

Monica and Mary are tactile souls – many's a Country Show steward got the hug of a lifetime from her, so warm was the embrace. I can picture the glint in her eye when she spotted someone she knew or, indeed, someone she wanted to know. In her flighty country determined way, she would make a bee-line for her "victim" and engulf him or her in her breath-taking bear hug. Those hugged by Monica could never forget the experience.

Sadly, when I took over as Editor of the *Farming Independent*, Mary's illness had taken hold and we were never to work together. Her postbag grew as news of her illness spread, and there was a chorus of calls for a collection of her life's work to be published.

And so it now is, as a living record of another time, seen through the unique eyes of Monica Carr.

Mairéad McGuinness
Editor, *Farming Independent*
September 1997

Mary Norton was born on a farm in Dunlavin, Co. Wicklow, on 28 August, 1922. Better known as a writer and broadcaster, she spent a large part of her early years farming the mixed farm until the 1950s when, almost by accident, she became a full-time freelance journalist.

"Nepotism" and "an aul slob of a grey mare" combined fortuitously to launch Mary in her writing career with the *Irish Independent*.

But the story of her transformation from Mary Norton to Monica Carr has its origins in table-tennis!

Mary's brother, Jim, and her late sister, Kitty, were very keen table-tennis players back in the late 1940s and 1950s and the task of sending reports of table-tennis matches to the *Leinster Leader* fell to Kitty.

So impressed was the paper with her beautifully written reports that they invited her to become their correspondent for West Wicklow. But Kitty had other plans. And so, brother Jim took on the task.

Later, a write-up submitted to the *Irish Independent* about a young farmers' visit to Denmark led to Jim's appointment as the paper's first Agricultural Correspondent. He went on to become the first Editor of the *Farming Independent*.

Mary stepped into his shoes on the local scene, reporting on matters relating to West Wicklow for the *Leinster Leader*, the *Carlow Nationalist* and the *Leinster Times*. All the while, she continued to farm.

One day Mary was working in the fields, closing drills with a borrowed mare – "the oul slob of a grey mare" which later went missing. To lose a mare in those days (or worse still to have a mare stolen) was a major social crime in rural Ireland of the 1950s.

Mary set out in search of the mare. Herself and her bike were the search party and she kept a detailed daily record of her three day ordeal in her diary.

The *Farming Independent* Editor, Jim, spotted the diary, billed it as "Country Diary" and added the by-line of Monica Carr to it – and the rest is history.

From then onwards, Mary wrote her much loved "Country Diary" under the pen-name of Monica Carr, and it is by this name she is so well-known throughout Ireland.

The Nortons' trick of keeping it in the family spilled over into the selection of the pen-name. Monica Carr was Mary's aunt, a Wicklow woman.

From that first "Country Diary", Monica Carr grew to become a household name.

She took to the airwaves on RTE radio in the mid-1960s and early 1970s on sponsored programmes – Nitrigin Eireann's farming programme, Livestock News Round-Up and later the *Farming Independent*'s own programme. Her characteristic voice became very well-known.

She had many a lively interview with Gay Byrne, including recounting the horror of a mugging experience she endured in Dublin.

So famous did Monica become that Brendan Grace and Rosaleen Linehan captured her in many humorous sketches as Cronica Maher.

But those who delved into her "Country Diary" each week in the *Farming Independent* did so for the way she portrayed farming and rural Ireland in less hectic and mechanised times and her absolute delight in its simplicity.

Her words brought back memories to those who came from farming stock and, for those who did not, they gave a delightful picture of country times, nature and how farmers manage through good and bad.

She is, and always will be, the "Queen of Rural Ireland".

MEAN, HUNGRY JANUARY!

"Don't be wishing your life away", my mother used to say when we wished for Easter as Christmas holidays neared an end, or in summer that it was already Christmas.

Time goes so fast nowadays that I know exactly what she meant. I didn't then, when a week, a month, a year, seemed interminable – a long saga of time to be got through – somehow.

Maturity – over-ripe maturity, indeed – does not prevent me, however, from deriving comfort from the fact that January, like all the months before and after, will "gallop".

It is my least favourite of the year's twelve children with its low skies, a dark and dreary world.

The sun, when it makes tentative efforts to show over the low hills, has only the cold stare of a headlight, slanted and shifty. Not an iota of heat in its brightness.

Threadbare hedges, low ditches brimming over, low-lying fields flooded into small lakes, the countryside stretches in famished lines to the hills. A mean, hungry world. But still, though we are in the trough of winter, it is losing its grip. The ebb is already on the wane.

The challenge of spring gets stronger by the day and we won't be far into this month of January until we notice, almost imperceptibly, the "cock's step" in the evenings, already indeed begun, even if we don't see it.

In a way there is honesty about a winter's landscape, leafless, flowerless, just brown-hedged fields and trees, their bare branches like pencil strokes against a background of grey sky.

Good to look out through the window of a warm kitchen until your breath fogs the glass and seals out the chilly world; to think back on an era when we didn't have great machinery to help us combat the elements.

Another life nowadays, but it helps my generation to reflect on our blessings when January moods take over, brooding nail-biting moods when the ache in your back, which is bearable in summer, becomes tyrannical and everyone you meet – as you wonder how in God's name all those bills will be met and just when, if ever, the sheep subsidy will arrive – gets on your nerves.

Old-fashioned (I admit it), a lot of modern poetry does not "turn me on". I like the stuff to rhyme – and so much today does not!

Something that does (rhyme, I mean) arrived in my letter box yesterday from a wonderful woman who sells jewellery from a street stand in a busy Leinster town. She penned these few lines as she stood in the freezing cold, customerless, her consolation and acceptance, her thoughts of vivid colour and the flowers which she loves passionately.

I admit to just skimming the lines at first, but the second time around, recollecting the conditions under which they were penned – the obvious underlying aching for warmth and love – I ached to pass them on to all those readers out there, whom I know will understand.

Colour me primrose, with dapples of blue,
Wrap me in freesias of multi-colour hue,
Sprinkle me in snowdrops and cobwebs of green,
Shelter me with orchids, the most exotic ever seen.
Gather me cowslips, with baby's breath too,
Then caress me with rose petals in fresh morning dew.

(January 1994)

SOUND THE HORN!

Every natural happening has its natural causes. But this does not in the least diminish the wonder.

Things seen and heard, no matter how often, retain their powers to mystify. I have lived through many Christmases and early Januarys but doubt there has ever been one so mild.

By pure chance, I drove straight into the New Year's Eve meet of our local foxhounds just as the field was about to move off to try a covert in a spinney three fields away and the huntsman's horn was the first thing I heard as I lowered the window of the car.

What a sound that plain polished copper tube makes! It speaks a language even more elemental than the chase of which it tells.

It is a thing of wonder and mystery, but the real wonder is that something so simple should possess so powerful a capacity to arouse feelings.

It is, after all, only capable of two notes and no amount of artistry in producing them could possibly add to their message unless the horn itself was magical.

Of its effects on others I can only guess. Of its effect on myself, I can write with experience. A concentration of awareness above all else on the distant sound, a heightened expectancy and curiosity, a magnetic attraction which drew me towards it in spirit, even as I sat in the car.

Good friends who have themselves hunted in youth are aware infinitely more than I of the thrilling effect of this sound that flows rather than cuts across a wintry countryside, penetrating woodland and vales as open ground. They argue that, knowing what it hails, it is simply an infusion of the primeval compulsion to hunt.

Madeleine, resting before tea in her nursing home bed after a lifetime of total involvement in country pursuits – horses, dogs, poultry – feels that it is the associated memories rather than the sound itself that stirs the blood.

A more than plausible explanation, certainly. After all, no sense evokes nostalgia as much as hearing. The bark of a dog down the valley on a frosty night, a cock crowing in some Grecian back-yard on the one and only trip that I made to that country, and I was transported back to childhood, to freezing mornings when central heating was something they had in America and electric blankets unheard of, or to racing across the dark yard on a January evening for an armful of logs or to the dairy for a jug of milk. Another life, but good to be jerked back now and then.

After the field had moved off, I continued on my road home, exalted. How is it, I pondered, when you reduce it to simple terms that the human breath expelled through pressed lips into simple pipes of copper, bronze, brass (or sometimes, I believe, silver) should have such power to arouse mankind in such varying circumstances?

Complex instruments, stringed or percussion, can inspire euphoria – that's a recognised fact – but only the hunting horn has the power to awake body as well as mind.

To date, life has not been hard on birds this year. The net of nuts on the bird-table outside my kitchen window is obviously a delicacy, but a flower pot of dripping, which I also hung out (with difficulty, I might add, to get it balanced) does not have the same appeal.

They will eat it if they are hungry enough, as my mother used to say when we refused turnip and cabbage. (How come children dislike vegetables and grow to love them in adulthood?)

(January 1992)

BOILING THE BONES

I would love to have the money for one of those gadgets which take the steam out of the kitchen. At this moment, mine is full of the revolting odour of boiling bones and, with the clothes-horse up there near the ceiling full of damp clothes, I assure you I would swap places with any of you.

One of the most sickening things which can happen a housewife occurred two hours ago. The wretched clothes-line broke and I have just finished re-washing the weekly quota of shirts and socks. Naturally this gives me a jaundiced view on life, but I feel better now that I have actually written it down and got it out of my system.

Another way of dispelling ill-humour is to break a plate – or a cup or a saucer, whichever you can spare best. I am told that the crash jerks you back in a flash.

I would love to have the spunk to try it but the very idea of deliberately breaking a bit of ware shocks my economical soul. One thing I do know, if I ever won the Sweep, it would be the first thing I would do.

I am boiling the bones because of something the butcher told me last week. He is convinced that modern women are a "dead loss" about using the cheaper cuts of meat.

Everybody today, he complains bitterly, wants sirloin steak. Nobody knows how to cook anything else. He believes that prime steaks will be completely unobtainable next Spring because of this.

There may be a lot of truth in what he says too, because modern housewives have become addicted to instant this and instant that and we may well have lost the art of getting the best out of food.

Certainly, I needed a rap on the knuckles. I have begun to rely on packet soup, for instance, without meaning it and was even becoming used to the taste. And there is no excuse for me with a solid fuel cooker on which the old stock-pot can always stand simmering away. A handful or two of pearl barley in it makes a great job of both the soup and your complexion.

You know, I remember clearing a nasty crop of pimples once by this simple expedient of eating soup made with pearl barley.

Living on a hill, as we do, may have its drawbacks but certainly not in this kind of weather. My heart bleeds for the unfortunates who have to contend with flooded fields and, even worse, flooded houses.

How the unlucky farmer in the next parish who had his silage pit swept away is going to overcome that blow beats me.

(January 1969)

WALK ON, WALK ON

Years roll on and, as they do, acts of irreversible consequence seem less attractive – unless the reasons for them are very strong.

To conquer exerts diminishing compulsion but, happily, to come and see still is a magnet in daily living.

Sharing, too, is all-important. Like a child who pesters the adult to "watch me", I found myself longing to show the three pink roses surprisingly still intact in spite of the frost to someone.

No human body available, I told Coffee, our resident Siamese cat, all about it as I carefully snipped them off and arranged them in the narrow-necked bud vase over the sink.

Same story, when I braved the chilly afternoon and strode down the hill for my constitutional. Walking, my knowledgeable friend assures me, is the best thing for hip- and back-aches.

Certainly it lifts the spirits, as did the glimpse of the unusual grey wagtail with a flash of bright yellow all along its undercarriage.

In the ditch alongside the road, a blackbird was working furiously, searching though the undergrowth, tossing great beakfuls over his shoulder like rescuers of buried humans after an earthquake.

What was he looking for? There was no one about to tell me or hazard a guess, but a golfing neighbour out for a stroll, with whom I joined forces further up the road, informed me that thrushes are becoming a menace rooting up the divots after caring, careful golfers have replaced them.

Nice fat juicy worms, without the bother of digging for them, are behind that little exercise of course, just as crows, if you've noticed, are becoming more and more common on roadways attracted by the multiplicity of carcases that fall victim to high speed – dogs, cats, rabbits, and their own brethren, indeed.

Interesting how birds and animals adapt to changing circumstances, isn't it? Do we humans do so as readily, I wonder?

Don't think so, although come to think of it, I find myself instinctively seeking the company of friends who talk up, without mumbling, now that the razor edge of my hearing has become blunted. Although I never realised this until it was pointed out by a third party. We live and learn, undoubtedly.

Like worms, while we are on the subject! With the natural drainage of our soil, we don't mind them as we should.

Spraying huge doses of slurry out on grass is putting toxins into the food chain, killing the worms that are working away down there aerating the soil.

It rarely dawns on us that the great rush of dark green grass which follows when it is cut leaves the soil panned out.

Great security about travelling by train in snowy, frosty weather. A trip across the country was a revelation, a real feeling of adventure tinged with guilt, siting there in the heated carriage as snow and sleet swirled past the window.

My heart went out to the car driver negotiating the black roads and twisty bridges outside. Only the very young like snow.

The purest sight before man and beast defile it, snow has a great capacity for creating filth in its wake. It lacks the antiseptic qualities of frost and brings no benefits to offset the harm it does. Baleful, when you are at its mercy, snowed up, trying to feed stock.

I detest the stuff, even if the transient beauty of bare bough powdered with white is quite beautiful. Suppose it is because my feet are too firmly anchored to the ground.

On television, snow has the overtones of reality which attaches to everything, conveyed by a medium which when you think of it, is mostly artificial. The reality is very different.

(January 1993)

WINDS OF CHANGE

How we change with the years? Incredible, isn't it? When we were young and care-free, we relished wild, windy nights.

Snuggling down in the feather mattress of the vast brass-balled iron bed which I shared with my sister, we rejoiced at every audible snarl of the hurricane outside, the crunch and creak of the wooden fences knocked over, the clang of slates flying off the roof, actually praying that one of the great beech trees lining the avenue would blow down so there would be no school next day because we couldn't get out.

So different from last week when I cowered at every sound, heart-sick at the crashing sound of a gable in the yard, stove in by the gale which ripped off yards of roof-cladding, leaving it poised at crazy angles.

Loose guttering swung and clanged before elements that had gone berserk, intent only on damage, certainly with no consideration for the cost of repair.

And aside altogether from the worry of monetary loss, there was fear that the roof of the house might go, fear for the road-users everywhere in such danger from falling trees, fear of possible flooding. And then as we listened to the late news on the bedside radio, how were the friends across in Galway faring?

Ah yes, the years bring more than wrinkles and aching knees. Concern, something that never bothered us overly, is now part of daily living, and shrugging it off becomes increasingly difficult too.

Surprisingly, the builder kept his word and came along next day and, while we were grateful for the speed with which he answered our distress call, his nonchalance was an irritant.

Free of any sense of hazard, he climbed up on the roof of the barn and stood there unchallenged by the height or by the gale's last lingering breaths as it whistled through the naked apple trees.

Holding the tape, he measured and noted with that faraway look in his eyes that indicated his personal aloofness from mundane matters like what it was all going to cost and the chances of the insurance policy covering any of the damage.

Strictly speaking, in this neck of the woods we don't have a leg to stand on, when it comes to feeling hard done by, I mean.

The unfortunates in Galway whose homes were flooded have the horrid, sickening smell of floodwater which lingers in homes for months. Infinitely worse, of course, was the earthquake in Japan, pictures of which really frighten the wits out of me.

In another life, I feel I must have been in an earthquake. Nothing else could have given me such terror of them, I believe. Imagine the ground opening under your feet, driving across a bridge with half of it gone, buckled, leaning down into nothingness.

And then I shake myself and look out at the familiar lawn field with the dozen or so early lambing ewes and their lambs, strong and sturdy, taking advantage of the bright – if admittedly still chilly – blast of sunshine. And thank the Lord for such pleasant places.

Hardship ahead? More than possible, and an ominous sign of hard weather is when the wood pigeons start feeding on the berries of the *cotoneaster horizontalis* across the garden wall.

I see two of them breakfasting and, knowing that these berries are not the favourite food of wood pigeons or any black birds, constituting what to them are iron rations, my heart sinks and I find myself wondering at what time the builder will arrive to batten down the hatches.

Worry . . . Is it possible for humans to live without worrying? Blessed if I can decide.

(January 1995)

ANOTHER AGE

Did one single person in the country leave a ribbon out on the window sill last night for St Brigid to bless and give it curative powers for headaches? Doubt it!

Unlikely, either, that anyone made oaten cakes in the shape of a cross for eating as you prayed to St Brigid today, her feast day.

Lá le Bhríde, February 1, when Raftery's noble soul stirred to be home in Mayo. And tomorrow we "throw candles away and eat our three meals by the light of the day".

Pishrogues? Maybe! Certainly seems so in this high tech age, but just as well somebody like myself brings them to your attention. We need reminding of how things were in another age.

The other day really was a perfect (admittedly early) spring day, and my friend had obviously succumbed to the feeling in the air when she sent a lovely card with a single daffodil and scribbled the words, "Yes, it really IS Spring".

We all want to share happiness, particularly that unexpected spurt of well-being which pulses through primitive earth-loving folk when the staggering miracle of another Spring suddenly makes itself evident – to the nose, the eye or ear, as the case may be.

I had sensed it myself twenty-four hours earlier when, on opening my bedroom window, I caught a few notes of that sweetest of all bird songs, a mistle thrush high up in the big naked copper beech at the road gate. Made my heart positively skip a beat as I listened.

Why? What chemistry of mind or body goes to work the instant those liquid notes of the first bird-song of the year reaches the ears? After all, as some cynic once remarked, if you turn a wet cork in a bottle-neck you get the same sound! Could it be that, deep down in our sub-conscious, we are scared that the miracle of spring won't happen, that this time the world may not come to life again.

And when it does – that mistle thrush, a flush of gold on the willow branches, a bud showing green after the dark days of December and January – we breathe a sign of relief, of thanksgiving, at being alive to experience such joy once again.

Unfortunately, my friend had been a trifle premature. Spring had not sprung. A flash in the pan, it seems, with flurries of sleet again darkening the world outside the kitchen window and a biting wind that would "take the nose off a brass monkey". Frost in the air in the evening making the very thought of venturing out to take a last look at some very pregnant ewes an unappealing prospect.

I felt sorry for the men and, to make up for the smugness in my heart (I'm not expected to do such work any more – and how I relish the thought), I sliced a lemon, plugged in the kettle and reached for the whiskey bottle – "hotties" for all hands, when they came in.

(February 1994)

CANDLEMAS LORE

If Candlemas be fair and bright,
Winter will have another flight,
But if Candlemas be wild and rain,
Winter is gone and won't come again.

Looking out at the pelting snow on Thursday ("plucking more geese in heaven", my grandmother used to tell us), it struck me that Candlemas had been fair and bright.

For once, the old rhyme has turned out accurately – even if only pure coincidence.

Indeed the day before, Wednesday, was a real "pet day", so much so it was difficult to pay any real heed to the Met forecast of hardship.

Luckily we did. The back kitchen was reassuringly piled high with logs and two full buckets of coal meant that we wouldn't be cold.

There was a full tea caddy – in the old days that was always grandfather's first thought. "See that there is enough tea, in case we're snowed in", he would order and while we no longer need the hundredweight bag of flour – in case we could not get out to buy bread – the deep freeze had plenty.

Ah yes, we were lucky and sitting by the roaring parlour fire, no other light except the flickering flames, the twilight world outside was magic and I felt ashamed of my luck.

So many out there cold and miserable and I didn't even have to put a foot outside the door that night.

Another one of the many compensations of age – as I am finding out daily. I suppose I should be grateful, thank my lucky stars – and the good Lord – at being able to appreciate and enjoy my lot, but typically the "worm in the rose" makes me restless, although guilty, I suppose, would be more accurate.

It was almost a relief when the men came in swearing about the snow and the lambing, which is in full swing, and a far cry I'm telling you from that picture on the landing of an old weather-beaten shepherd leaning on his crook with a healthy lamb under one arm and the ewe standing quietly at his feet looking up lovingly.

Don't ask me where that particular picture came from. It's been here all my life in this house, painted by someone called Seymour, back in 1850 (if the inscription is accurate). A romantic, poetical vision of lambing not anything like the reality you'll find today.

Things change so with the years. Paperwork is now as great a part of farming as any of the seasonal tasks of tilling, silage-making or, at this time of the year, lambing.

Indeed paperwork could be described as THE most important part. It always was, of course, although we didn't recognise it, but farmers who kept accounts and "did up" their books regularly were the people who "got on". Took us a while to recognise this, unfortunately.

The lighter side of paperwork these days is Valentine card sending, I notice. The young people are head, neck and heels into it. A ferocious waste of money, I feel it is, but then I was brought up hard, I suppose, and it's never easy to teach an old dog new tricks.

The card shops make money out of it, anyway, and haven't they got to make a living too? Who, I wonder, buys the huge cards or the red and white satin-hearted affairs which cost, many of them, as much as £10.

Soon it will be Pancake Day, Shrove, when the old people ate a prodigious feed of pancakes in preparation for the fasting of Lent.

A real laugh nowadays, telling the young about the black tea and butterless bread and one full meal only and "two collations". Funny word, collation! Real business it was weighing the bread.

Did any of us keep the fast strictly, I wonder? I did and now I don't have to! Life, as I said earlier, could be worse.

(February 1991)

SEÁN'S DILEMMA

The bliss of slumping in front of a crackling log fire on a raw February evening is a treat which seldom comes our way in these days of endless meetings and projects, not to mention artificial heat.

Switching on the electric fire for the hour or so one can spare to spend in the parlour always seems more sensible, but this morning, for some unaccountable reason, the men had got around at last to sawing up the pile of boughs – a mixed collection – which has been cluttering up the barn since last Spring, and the thrill of having sticks to burn again prompted me to take the night off and light the fire.

A Western film on the TV kept the men anchored in the kitchen, so I had the room to myself, another unaccustomed luxury. Like a miser counting his gold, I carefully selected my next stick, a bit of apple wood, and placed it carefully on the well-established glowing red bed of thorn. The perfume of the wood filled the room and, outside in the hay shed where grandfather has scooped out a clearing to make a cosy kennel, Ginger, the new sheepdog, barked suddenly and the chain which held his collar rattled.

It was all so peaceful in that still room with only the lively glowing fire for company, and my thoughts ranged on a million things to the days when we were young, without pain or ache, and life

– like a blown-up balloon in a strong wind – was tugging and pulling at the cord we held in the tough, hard confident hands of youth.

Tough and hard though they were, they were not always strong enough to hold on to the string, and there have been disappointments and reverses galore over the years. Automatically I think of my greatest worry at the moment, my son Sean who is going through a trying period, for him and for us, of wondering loudly and at length whether he was wise to stay at home and farm.

His latest threat of emigrating to Australia is the cause of many sleepless nights for Tom and myself but, mother-like, I find excuses which stupidly, in a futile attempt to comfort Tom, I trot forth, bringing down an avalanche of wrath on my head in the process.

Ah well! It will soon be March, one month nearer the summer when we shall hear again the quivering song of the lark and the thrush in the early morning.

As it is, the sun is dropping to rest a little earlier every day over there in the west behind Church Hill and the flood of amber through the scullery windows lingers that bit longer. The dusk, too, is lengthening and the shadows becoming coloured again. All over the lawn, there are clumps of snowdrops.

Why am I moaning?

Rowan Lady calved yesterday, a lovely little heifer and the Biestings tart I made for the tea – my first attempt at this dish – was an unqualified success.

Life may have conditioned me to accept disappointments, but it has also shown me that true happiness lies in the accomplishment of seemingly insignificant things like turning out a perfect Biestings tart.

(February 1970)

ROOKS BUILD IN SPRING

Do you know something? I've come to the conclusion that we humans, in spite of all the modern technology, are only in what my father used to call "the halfpenny place" to many species – rooks in particular I'm thinking of now.

Our resident "parish" of rooks began building two weeks ago. Tradition goes that the date for building should be March 1, but our "laddibucks" are already half way through their housing programme.

My very favourite spring relaxation is watching this process and I never cease to count my blessings as I watch the rookery from a grandstand view from the sink. It makes even preparing turnip bearable, a job I detest as much as I enjoy mashed turnip with lots of pepper and a crispy-edged chop. Indeed it becomes almost enjoyable, because I can forget the chore as I stand there and stare.

Twenty years ago, the largest contingent of our birds nested in droves on the other side of the house. There was a huge crown elm there, the sort once used for wooden wheel hubs because it did not split. I recall being surprised as I watched the birds taking sticks from their old nests in the elm and carrying them across the road to build in the younger plantation, now a mature standing of trees.

Old Nick Thomas, "the best man to 'lay' a hedge in five parishes" – hopefully he is getting a chance of doing his favourite job in Heaven – forecast the demise of that elm. "We'll have a mess to clear up before long", he warned us.

A couple of months, I suppose, went by and sure enough, first windy night down came the giant elm crashing through the other trees. Its roots had broken underground, in a circle of earth, and fibre still stood eight feet tall.

Other birds I recall had not heeded the warning creaks – or maybe rooks are the only ones with this in-built radar.

Conifers, with which this country abounds, make good nesting sites but are hungry woods for young birds. Where there are oaks there are moths and caterpillars on the leaves by the end of May, and the lighter calls of the younger rooks feeding way up in an oak is clearly discernible to an attuned ear.

Perish the day when deafness stops me hearing that and the other Spring sounds that raise your heart. Hopefully, I'll be up talking hedges with Nick Thomas by then.

The greatest thrill for me during much of this past grand month of February has been the afternoon hours pottering in the garden or strolling across the fields.

Demands, thankfully, are lighter than they were and, thankfully too, I have sense enough to appreciate the real fulfilment of "standing and staring".

When one can get really absorbed shutting out the cares and worries of daily life, a spell of just "gawking" is as good, if not better, than a session of reflexology.

Which, incidentally, if you've never had a "go", is a big blank in your life. Superb experience and the well-being afterwards has to be experienced to be believed ...

'Course I know well that it "takes all sorts to make the world" and others may not derive the benefits I get from reflexology, but it's definitely my favourite treat.

(March 1993)

ANIMAL WELFARE

I met a farmer recently who admits that there is "room for improvement" in the treatment of animals by farmers in general. Particularly in the past.

Same man is a rarity. He has the distinction of being the very first I have come across to accept liability. Usual thing is for both sides, farmers and the extremists of the anti-cruelty lobby, to declare themselves "whiter than white". Which of course is quite wrong.

There is a vast grey area in every battle, but then I also know a man who declares that one simply can't afford to see both sides of a war because it stops you from winning.

To people like ourselves who have been subjected to, or enjoyed (you take your pick), the joyous barbarism of a rural childhood, there is an immense amount of nonsense and over-reaction to the welfare of animals.

From early on, we snared rabbits, caught tadpoles and kept them in jam-jars (often, I'm ashamed to admit, forgetting them), thrilled at sight of the red fox racing across the Six Acres, hounds in full cry, charged home from school on pig-killing days, and even found nothing offensive in cattle-skulling.

It was all part of everyday living – of farming practice in an era before parents felt a compulsion (thanks to peer-pressure, of course) to fill their children's waking hours with improving pastimes, riding lessons, trombone and flute playing, organised swimming, in the after-school hours that were magic times for country children brought up like us in the Twenties and Thirties.

Thinking about the incredible pressure parents of today are under to entertain and educate offspring, I often think that the lack of training, the lack of entertainment for children – which was the norm in our days – was a good thing.

Home-spun knowledge, country lore, the names of birds and weeds and the types of soil in different fields, best for this crop or that, was rarely actually taught us – it just soaked in through the pores.

It's easy, of course, to be romantic about childhood, once you are far enough away to have forgotten the discomforts, the poverty, the cold and the isolation.

These past few days of colder-than-heretofore winter weather is all I need to pull me out of the nostalgia trap. Those icy sheets over the feather mattress, the freezing loo – down that picturesque little path at the bottom of the garden – Gr-r-r-r-r-r!

The whiff of "ordinary" danger (as distinct from the infinitely worse variety from video nasties and drug peddlers today) did us no harm.

When you are brought up near a stream that's really running fast, you know when to paddle and when not. Nothing really frightened us because you had to be out in the dark in all weathers. People close to you had to be out in it and they weren't frightened, so they didn't pass on fear.

(March 1995)

GOING OUT LIKE A LION . . .

The retired British major who lived down the road from us as children prefaced most of his comments to my father with "By George".

Always made us laugh. We never knew, nor cared, who "George" was, but it became a family saying, and "By George" but March is certainly fulfilling the old country belief of "going out like a lion".

At a funeral in a bleak Co. Wicklow graveyard during the past week, I swear the cold of the east wind sweeping down from Lugnaquilla would literally "take the nose off a brass monkey".

Covered with snow, "Lug" (as we locals always call the mountain) was, for the first time this year too. But this morning it was milder, even a blast of deceptively warm sunshine when I was out quite early, enough to bring the resting sheep back to life.

And I watched as one by one, they climbed stiffly to their feet to stand patiently while toy-like lambs sucked eagerly.

You could say, I suppose, that I did something similar myself, 20 minutes later inside in the warm kitchen facing a daddy-bear-sized bowl of steaming hot pinhead oatmeal porridge.

Greatest breakfast in the world on a chilly morning – and nothing better than a daily ration of the stuff for your heart.

And heart medicine is something which the residents of Kill, Co. Kildare, need in large quantities at this time – if the proposed dump there for Dublin goes ahead.

Ferocious problem finding suitable sites for the appalling amount – and frightening types of litter – that must be disposed of in this disposable world of 1992.

No-one wants a dump on their doorstep. That goes without question, but proximity to a main water supply – in this instance, for the city of Dublin – is surely a crazy idea. Money – lust for it, lack of it – one as bad as the other – is presumably at the root of this particular evil.

Unfortunates who are immediately affected can only see their own side – a typical human reaction, of course, and my heart (porridge and all at this precise moment) aches in sympathy for friends who have slaved all their lives to get stud farms and homes into shape. They are now faced with the shattering prospect of a huge dump (with presumably the chances of toxic waste often included – in spite of the best-laid schemes, this is bound to happen) on their doorsteps.

The world has changed so much. Trite comment, I know, but has it ever struck you there is no longer any real darkness? Somebody should organise a Society for the Protection of the Night because, like the desecration of the landscape, the quality of the night has deteriorated immeasurably.

Think about it! When the sun has set and the last deepening residue of daylight faded, Keats' "embalmed darkness" is now a rare commodity.

Even on clear nights, artificial radiance intrudes where no radiance should be. This is not unpleasant but, indeed, most useful because most of us have lost the old power country people had of being well able to see in the dark. But when you think about it, neither is it natural.

The nocturnal face of our countryside reflects a lot of awfulness. Like a glow from a volcano, towns and cities viewed from a distance are eternally lit up to await the dawn.

Garish lighting everywhere, which gives the sky at night a blotched polychrome appearance – even from our yard, still happily sunk deep in rurality.

Modern lighting seems symbolic of modern technology, reducing all things to one level, revealing the form without the life and soul of what it touches.

Behind the wheel of a car is a great place to reflect on these sort of things. If I were a badger, a fox, an owl – any creature with a vested interest in genuine darkness – I would look on all this lit-up world with even more distaste than I do as a representative of *Homo Sapiens*, which naturally makes me wonder if we are so sapient after all.

(March 1992)

DOGS IN THE KITCHEN

Mild weather is a bonus from the Lord for which we cannot be sufficiently grateful, but Heavens, the mud! The kitchen floor is like a skating rink half an hour after it has been washed and, as for the gateways, they are so badly poached that negotiating them is like wading through a snowdrift.

I barred the collies from the house in the hope that it might improve matters but it was a waste of time. Shep obeyed the injunction reasonably well but, the minute my back was turned, Grandfather opened the door for Bruno and I came back inside to find him stretched out in front of the cooker, a trail of muddy paw-marks reaching over to the door.

The guilty air of man and dog when I catch them would be laughable if I had someone to wash the floor for me. As it is, I try not to "create" too much, but non-stop floor-washing is a demoralising job calculated to make tempers reach boiling point over-quickly.

The only gateway on the farm which is passable is the one into the Pike Field where, two Springs ago, Tom buried the remains of old Mick Quinn's brick-walled cottage. Broken brick sets like cement after even one summer.

It was when they were bulldozing the ditch that they had unearthed the portion of brick wall, completely buried under nearly seventy years of summer growth and winter frosts and snows. Had it not been for Grandfather's memory of old Julia Quinn's thick slices of soda bread and honey, we would never have known that the same brick wall was once part of the "best mitching house in two counties".

Television, and the speed of the Sixties and Seventies which has permeated even into remote regions like these, have finished the mitching era for ever.

The days of story-telling and card-playing in neighbours' houses is a thing of the past and who can blame people of Grandfather's generation for wondering what on earth we do with all the time saved today by comparison with when water was carried half a mile in a bucket and churning the butter for the household often took as much as four hours on a winter's morning.

Getting back to the present, the Vet was telling us yesterday morning that they will soon be regarding themselves as blacksmiths with all the foot trouble they are attending.

The acid from the effluent from the silage is responsible, it seems, and Friesians are the worst sufferers. Their white feet are not as hardy as the Shorthorn hooves. The day is coming, apparently, when cows will be shod just like horses.

When you think of it, that is only the wheel going full circle. Cattle were shod in the old days, as that peculiar shoe hanging in the pub in the village tells us.

I cannot say that the idea is appealing, and from the condition of the men when they came in this morning after poulticing a cow's foot where gravel had worked up a solid inch, shoeing a horse will be chicken-feed to shoeing a cow.

(March 1975)

CYCLING IN APRIL

April, my favourite month – and I find myself this year disturbingly grateful at being alive to savour yet another magical experience.

Because so it is. And marvellous too that I'm still able to cycle. A fine morning in April is one of those times in life when a bicycle becomes more than a mere method of locomotion, and pedalling my trusty High Nelly out the bog road (the un-potholey portion) I catch myself remembering constantly the rapture behind Beeching's song:

> Oh bird, see; see bird I fly,
> Is this, is this your joy?

Funny, isn't it, how odd stanzas of long forgotten poems and songs remain in the mind, buried until dredged up by some experience? Like young lambs bleating behind the hedge of a sunny field, catkins dripping from silver birches, a lane white with hawthorn, or the peachy perfume of gorse that fills the nostrils as you cycle past. Another couple of lines I love are:

> Two ducks on a pond,
> a green bank beyond.
> What a thing to remember for years,
> to remember with tears.

Hares go mad in March but it is the April air that has gone to my head, I think. That air which is full of birdsong, so soft and continuous, it is hardly noticeable unless you stop and listen!

I try to identify the singers as I peg clothes out on the line, a chore which I normally detest – but not on a fine April morning. The urgent, frequent cry of the chiff-chaff high up in the tree-tops, stopping only as it flits to another branch. The rasping note of the tits. The sudden startled trill of a wren. And, to me, the always comforting cawing of the rooks.

I swear I could watch crows for an hour. Wonderful birds going about their business of living – for all the world like ourselves. Ah yes, perish the day if the magic, the wonder of an April day, disappears for me.

On the more practical side, inside in the kitchen April is a great pork month. Time was when we only ate pork when there was an "R" in the month. Pre-refrigeration days, of course.

A friend was eulogising only yesterday on the merits of a loin of pork cooked with grated lemon rind but there are dozens of ways in the Bord Bia new recipe cards which are at present in the shops.

The Bord's food advisory service also advises us not to overlook the inexpensive but extremely tasty belly of pork which can adapt to lots of dishes. Great attraction of the belly of pork is the big expanse of crackling – and do you know anyone who doesn't enjoy crackling?

Patsy Lawlor, former ICA National President, tackled me the other day about the hardness of butter. A devotee of butter like myself – she wouldn't dream of using any of the spreads – she finds it hard to understand why the butter remains hard even when left out overnight in a warm kitchen.

(April 1995)

POLISHING & SUPERSTITION

A long line of family washing, drying before your eyes on a bright, windy April morning, could be described as the height of happiness.

Idea makes you scoff? Could happen, I suppose, but at this precise moment the sight fills me with enormous satisfaction, and satisfaction is akin to happiness after all. Who said so? No philosopher that I know of, but who cares about philosophers when the gut feeling is right!

Funny thing about housework, soul-destroying stuff usually, but immensely rewarding at times. Like my friend who absolutely adores polishing good furniture.

Calling in on her the other morning I found her tré na céile looking for a favourite polishing rag. When it finally came to light, it turned out to be a piece of an old cotton shirt.

"There's something about the texture that makes polishing a pleasure", she informed me clutching the length of blue and white cotton as if it were her best silk slip.

Something, incidentally, I'd love to possess, pure silk underwear – the sort that wouldn't cling to your skirt and would stay in place decorously when riding "High Nelly" around corners on windy mornings.

What was it my father, God rest the man, used to say when he was the unwilling recipient of long garbled stories, in which a man like him, totally involved in horses, greyhounds and all aspects of farming, was not remotely interested? "If it is your hour for confessin', it's not my hour for hearin'", he would retort, stamping off to a quiet place out of reach of "talking women and prattlin' children".

The miracle is that I'm not totally "screwed up" as they say today, after an upbringing in which no-one ever heard of Dr Spock or the importance of listening to children and never, ever laying a hand on them.

The whip which he used in the pony trap was my father's favourite weapon. He had the marvellous ability to crack it and, without really hurting, let you feel the bite of it across the bare legs. Oddly, we never felt any lasting resentment. Wonder why?

Maybe because he never "held things in" afterwards. Or would it have been the respect we had for him that stopped us sulking? Sulking, I have discovered, is a widely-used weapon by young people today and the majority of parents, alas, are unable to accept the cold war so they succumb and the youngsters consequently get away with murder.

So delightfully easy to "prate" when one is on the other side of 60. One of the few compensations, depending how you look at it, one could say.

Watching the men out in the yard this morning loading a bullock for the mart, I suddenly bethought myself of an old superstition which an old cattle dealer at home had. He would never try a second time with an animal that didn't enter the wagon (as it was in those days) convinced that something would happen if he insisted. Happily it didn't work out this morning as there were three different attempts before the animal was loaded.

Another superstition was to keep a billy goat in the cow house to drive away the germs of *Brucella Abortus*. This was considered "entertaining the devil" who would drive away the disease before him. It was customary to run a donkey with the dairy herd in another parish to prevent abortion, where they considered the billy goat good for keeping ringworm at bay.

They hated it at home if anyone offered to buy your working dog. This was considered very unlucky, as was having a woman present at the birth when a mare was foaling. (I can just imagine the faces of some female stud owners at that!)

Never hang a horseshoe ends downwards or the luck will fall out, though another school of thought maintained if they were hung upwards the devil would sit in it.

Finally, the farmer and his new wife always must cross the threshold of their farmhouse for the first time side by side to ensure they will "work well in double harness".

(April 1992)

HOLY WEEK

Holy Week – how quickly Lent has flown by! When I was young and fasting was very much part of life for young and old, Lent crept by on leaden feet.

Nobody "does the fast" nowadays, I imagine, so the "Holy Season" means little.

Pity! The thrill of looking forward to digging teeth into the marshmallow of an Easter egg after seven long weeks of abstinence is something too few children today will experience. For us it was heaven, but then we were so easily pleased.

Something else I'm thinking about is the annual spring-cleaning of the parlour carpet which always took place on Good Friday.

A square surrounded by a two-foot border of painted board, it was rolled up, carried out to the lawn and beaten solidly for an hour with sally rods.

Everyone took a hand and the dust flew high and, indoors, the unfortunate servant girl – who worked for only 10 shillings a week plus the "run of her beak" – wielded a mighty scrubbing brush on the bare boards and mopped up the wet with a flannel cut from worn-out underpants or combinations (which were the "in" thing of the time), her hands red and swollen from the harsh washing soda.

A sprinkling of Jeyes fluid to get rid of any winter residue remaining, before the carpet was returned, made the house smell like the area around the dipping tub after the sheep had gone through it but no one objected.

That was an era when having the hens at "full lay" at Easter time was considered a cause of great congratulation if they were and real dismay if they weren't.

Going to the various church services throughout the week, conversation was about "clockin' hens" and having a clutch of Easter chicks was something every woman worth her salt aimed at.

How well I remember a bantam bringing out five chicks on a Holy Thursday back in the Thirties. Fascinating little things they were, like fat bumble bees running in to take shelter under the fluffed-out feathers of their miniature mother, who gave me a jolly hard peck, actually drawing blood, when I ventured to extricate one to show a schoolmate.

Probably why I remember it so vividly! Like the satisfying business of blowing eggs to decorate an Easter tree. That was something a German neighbour taught us and what an interesting table decoration a branch laden with coloured eggs makes.

April was always the time of year too for treating furniture for woodworm. Looking back, it seems that all the houses in the countryside had woodwormy chairs and sofas because every housewife did the job as a routine part of spring cleaning.

There are all sorts of preparations available today, complete with nozzle for squeezing into the telltale holes, but I still go for the old-fashioned half Jeyes fluid, half paraffin oil treatment of half a century ago.

The trick is to lob plenty of the fluid into and around the woodworm holes, paying particular attention to any soft wood, like the backs of cabinets, which often are made of timber inferior to the mahogany sides and fronts of furniture.

(April 1991)

GOOD FRIDAY

Good Friday was a glorious April morning that ignited the nesting instinct inherent (if mostly dormant) in all women – even if some of us refuse to acknowledge the feeling. Nothing seemed a trouble. I had already made a list of jobs for the day, and the lobby window, awkwardly placed for access to clean, was first on the agenda.

Balancing on the step-ladder, I leaned out as far as I could reach, rubbing vigorously at the winter's grime, the sunshine-bathed countryside spread before me, when into view, around the corner of the twisting road down in the valley, came a hearse followed by a short procession of mourning cars. Pausing to mouth a prayer (and wonder who had died), it struck me what an appropriate day it was out of all in the year to "shuffle off".

No-one wants to die. That goes without saying, but somehow Easter, the season of new life when the earth and everything in it is burgeoning, is the time I would like if I had my choice.

Foolish notions – we all go when it is ordained for us, but for a split few seconds the thought of my return there one day didn't seem too awful at all.

Not just yet, Lord! There was a mountain of housework to be done and this gleaming window only the beginning.

Funny how the mind works? Good Friday was always the day set aside for planting the early potatoes and for beating the carpet.

In those pre-carpet sweeper days (a twig of green-bristled broom the usual method of cleaning), the square of Axminster was lifted off the floor every Good Friday and beaten thoroughly with ash plants, while the bare square of boards in the parlour was scrubbed with washing soda and sunlight soap, and the border of painted boards all around given a "good waxing".

It was also the day for dealing with woodworm which we did by squirting a mixture of Jeyes fluid and paraffin oil into the holes, and no better cure, as I can vouch, by looking at the old grandfather chair on which I am typing this diary. Riddled it was, for a few seasons, but the pungent Jeyes did the trick.

(April 1988)

WATER EVERYWHERE . . .

"All in an April evening" – with a vengeance. Two near-dead lambs beside the cooker in the kitchen, silage and hay almost cut, and now non-stop driving rain that turned the yard into a small river and the Lawn Field – which we were hoping to till tomorrow – into a bog.

Out through the road gate the water poured, taking with it bits of straw and diesel spillages that turned the muddy surface greeny-blue. Dashing across to the fuel-house for supplies, the sound on the galvanised roof was like devils playing bodhráns and apprehensively, as I filled the basket, I eyed the felt roof of the back kitchen.

Was I imagining the sagging patch to the left? Was there water lying there? Perish the thought, but we should have seen to it months ago when the housing grants were available – where the money would come from now is anyone's guess.

The lane up to the house was another worry. Full of potholes since the snow, and the bulk tank playing further havoc every morning, it was in a sorry state, a danger to man, beast and vehicle. Too easy I'd been. A bit more nagging would have got those holes filled with big stones and then smaller chippings, but I'd thrown in the sponge and listened to the vague promises of the job being done "one of these days when there was time".

Regret for mistakes – an everyday story for all of us I'm afraid, and regrettably it's so difficult to learn. Reading directions, for instance. Like so many, I'm bad at studying the small print and, with such dishonesty at every level nowadays, one should never neglect this important angle of buying anything.

The plumber recommended an instant electric shower and foolishly I took his advice, leaving him to get on with it, after the initial visit to the big local supplier where I was assured that the model I was paying for was "perfect for the job".

It wasn't, but only now am I finding this out. A mixer shower would have been right for my household. The trickle that comes out at the moment, when you want a good hot shower, is pathetic . . . The expert who came to see for himself, after I complained, was charming, understood my frustration, sympathised, but felt I "should have read the booklet before deciding".

Luckily, before I pierced the top of a tin of silicone – to dab on the back of a mirror before sticking it (with grab tabs) on the newly tiled bathroom – I discovered that a gun was needed. That small supplier "made no bones" about returning my money – which means that he retains my custom.

Must stop griping or I'll be getting dandruff – as the old song puts it.

(April 1987)

APRIL HURRIES AWAY . . .

It was reassuring the other day to hear a group of young people remark on how speedily April had flown. Somehow one is inclined to think that time goes quickly only for adults.

Personally I can't credit that Friday is the beginning of May, when traditionally, no matter how fine the weather, one must never "cast a clout until May was out".

Clouts in our family meant winter vests and those horrid grey wool ribbed knee-socks which we ached to shed in favour of cotton dresses and sandals. And what a great day it was when we were finally allowed to get into our summer clothes, most of the dresses sporting the let-down marks on the end of skirts, out of which we had grown since September.

There is no real demarcation line today. Young people wear whatever suits them, light flimsy skirts with thick wool jumpers and Doc Martin boots, the sort only "labourers" wore in the old days.

Actually at this time of year at Punchestown – which was, in this neck of the woods, only second to Christmas in the Thirties, Forties and Fifties – the very idea of attending in comfortable clothes, gloveless, hatless, and flat-heeled, was something we never contemplated. You dressed up for "the Races" as you did for Mass on Sunday, suffering headaches from the unaccustomed pressure of hats – something you accepted uncomplaining.

Fashion today, ludicrous as much of it may seem, is great by comparison, and I have the height of respect for the way comfort comes first with youth.

Something else I rejoice in is being alive for another May. At one time, it was considered unlucky to marry in May. Wonder why? To me, the month is reminiscent of a young shy bride (if there are any left in 1992), bedecked from head to toe in white, because white is synonymous with May.

The blossom on the thorn, filling the air as you walk past with the perfume of coming summer, is white – although, in a way, white is too cold a word for the general creaminess of May blossom and the delicate wild parsley in the ditches underneath.

Neither are the hundreds of dandelion clocks white – as snow is white – and the apple blossom, at its very best just now, is tinged with shell-pink or ivory.

Not for nothing, when you think about it, did May earn her antique title of "lusty". Every place holds in it the feeling of life stirring, of pulsating growth, heard if still unseen.

There are rustlings and scufflings in the hedges which mean young birds being fed, taking their first timorous flights from the nest, scrambling back to safety in wild efforts from branch to branch.

My Churchtown, Co. Dublin, friend is thrilled to bits about the baby robins in her garden shed. "So absolutely perfect to first see them on Good Friday", she told me excitedly on the telephone, recalling the old tale about the robin's breast stained with blood from trying to extract the nails from the hands of the Lord.

But it was all shattered when a cat got in "behind her back" and put paid to the pretty scene.

Getting back to hawthorn, Grandmother Carr's recipe book has an entire page devoted to the merit of the hawthorn blossom as a heart tonic. Any homeopathic chemist can supply hawthorn liquid, which she called "a very mild remedy, slow to take effect but effective eventually" and, great thing about it, one can continue taking it without the least risk of harm.

She also recommends it for curing dropsy, "particularly when this condition is associated with heart trouble, as it often is".

(April 1992)

FAMILY WOES

My neighbour, Phyllis Murphy, mother of six, and the most available and comforting shoulder to cry on when my family gets too much for me, says any mother who tells you that her teen-age children give no trouble is deliberately fooling herself.

Personally, I go a step further and call it "lying", but what does a name matter when one is up to one's neck worrying about one's own offspring?

Were we as self-assertive and demanding as our children are? I wish I could honestly remember! We certainly did not have all the comforts and facilities they take for granted, but that is not really their fault and, underneath, did we give our parents as much trouble in a different way?

I have an idea that we were every bit as thoughtless and selfish and, looking back, I think I can recollect a period when I considered my unfortunate mother, God be good to the woman, the greatest tyrant and the greatest fool on God's earth.

I wish it would come back to me exactly when I got over that particular phase. It would be such a comfort just now, when my own "beauties" have obviously got a similar opinion of me.

Ah well, it could be worse I suppose, and Spring is finally here this week so depression cannot last.

Everything in heaven and earth proclaims the news – from the immediately obvious, like the way the grass is coming, to the catkins dripping from the silver birches in the Mill Field and the primroses starring every ditch.

The balmy air as I work in the garden is full of bird song, so soft and continuous as hardly to be noticeable, unless you stop and listen. I do – and the invisible lark, unbearably sweet, is the first to register. And then there is the rasping note of some tits and the sudden startled trill of a wren.

Trees and hedges are sprouting a delicate green veil and we are happy to welcome the season which embraces all of us, young and old, pretty and plain, in her own tender loveliness. Generous where all other youth is selfish, she makes us feel young in rejoicing instead of old in contrast, and blossoms in our tired worried hearts until, for a precious half hour, the world begins anew for us as for every flower on earth.

(May 1979)

THE SPRING SHOW

Mulling over the Spring Show and what I like best about it, three things come to mind.

Number one, the perfume of the RDS wallflowers. Quite special I always feel . . . especially after a shower when the scent really gets to you and memories of Maytime "Forty Hours", with bundles of multicoloured wallflowers clutched in hot little hands during the "endless" Litany of the Saints, flood the mind.

Second thing I love is the opportunity it gives of meeting people, friends, old and new, everywhere and that marvellous feeling of being really at home in Dublin, something that very few country folk experience at any other time of the year.

The Army band in the marquee on the lawn is something else I always enjoy and, oh yes, chatting with farm workers up at the show to collect their Long Service Awards on the Thursday.

What tales those old-timers have to tell and, twenty years ago, when many of them vividly remembered the "bad old days" – of sleeping rough on draughty lofts, washing in ice-cold water and trudging daily, from six to six, after a pair of horses – the stories were often horrific.

Incredible when you think back of the changes in farming. No century has seen so many, that's for sure. Take spraying for weeds, for instance.

To this day, I remember clearly my father slumped in despair in his big leather armchair in the family kitchen announcing that "the fly has destroyed the turnip crop".

I can see the scene, father old and grey-faced with worry in his early forties, mother wiping the flour from her hands as she lifted a soda-cake into the pot-oven, looking anxiously at him, out of her mind trying to think of something consoling to say.

We children were playing around on the floor, but young as I was I knew that a terrible thing had happened as he wearily dragged himself to his feet to set out to 'drill them again'.

Ready-dressed seed put an end to the flea beetle, which always came suddenly, worked overnight on young seedlings and often, when a man didn't go up to the field for a day or two, the turnips – which were a mighty important crop in those days – would have come and gone.

Huge swing indeed from being pretty powerless to having chemicals to deal with just about every insect, weed or disease you could name. No wonder you are asked to pay more for organically-grown produce. Only right with such a high risk factor.

Out on the hill for a stroll yesterday afternoon (and yes, I DID thank the Lord for my luck having such a glorious May world on my doorstep and being able to walk and enjoy it), the amount of chrome yellow rape on field, hill and headland stretching everywhere in huge swathes reminded me of those pre-herbicide days when there were meadows at this time of the year every bit as dazzlingly bright but with buttercups.

Very few cowslips nowadays, although I did "come on" several healthy clumps on a ditch near Calverstown, The Curragh, during the week. Couldn't believe my eyes!

(May 1991)

GLORIOUS MAY

Every year, in the glorious month of May, I get the urge to stop the march of time. If we could have eight weeks in May, how wonderful it would be.

Pink chestnuts in their supreme glory, apple trees a froth of blossom, the intense green of the lawn and the dawn chorus this morning.

And it wasn't that I was wakeful either. Chance woke me to the bliss of it and, through the wide open bedroom window, it began with the lonely cry of the curlew, then the shrill pipe of the redshank before the blackbird started his solo.

A real memory jerker this time of the year – of rearing turkey poults, ducklings and chickens. What a business it was in the Thirties and Forties and even later.

Incessant watchfulness for their first few weeks of life for turkeys and ducklings. Chickens were always that bit hardier, but everything, it seemed, was a trouble to the others.

Intense sunshine on their heads would turn them giddy, we believed, so there had to be a protective board or awning under which they could creep.

The unexpected shower wetted their feathers in another dangerous way. For warmth afterwards, they were inclined to huddle together and thus contract chills, so we had to keep them on the move until their feathers dried.

May was always the time when the yard was full of young things. How well I recall tearing round the countryside on my bike when a clocking hen "riz" from her clutch of eggs and one so desperately needed a surrogate mum.

I always felt sorry for the poor hen that brought out a clutch of ducklings. Her family became such alien creatures in such a short time. Growing up for ducklings is a business requiring limitless energy and unending activity.

Clucking desperately, she would warn her brood of the danger which water, of course, would have been to chicks, but they just ignored her.

Quite a while it took for the poor mother to stand back and recognise that creatures on whom so much time (four long weeks of hatching for ducks) had been lavished were a different species.

(May 1988)

SUMMER BLOOMING

There was no hesitation about "casting clouts" this past week. It was suddenly high summer, and when you managed to forget the seed shrivelling in the ground – barley and oats in the fields, flowers, vegetables, and the actual lawn in the garden – we revelled.

No more wonderful time of the year, with all growing things still young, than the merry month of May – when the weather behaves. Behaves?

Not the right word, because of course, moisture is needed for the growing things. "A wet and windy May fills the barn with corn and hay" is still true, but all must admit it's been a magic week.

Those first few minutes in the mornings before anyone else is up, out there in the dew-drenched garden in my nightdress, the perfume of the lilac is heart-breaking.

Many, many years ago, I was courted under lilac trees – on the way home from May Devotions. Honestly cannot remember who the particular "boy" was. It's like looking back through a veil, but the languorous warmth of summer that breathed from the heavy lilac cones over our heads is still a treasured memory.

Makes me feel young again, and while I am perfectly happy at this present stage of living – and now I want to reassure anyone who hates the idea of growing old – there is a unique sweetness about youth that is good to recall now and then.

Apart from the perfume, the most marvellous thing about lilac is the way it continues to grow and flourish in deserted places.

You've seen it, I'm sure, decorating and scenting the air alongside country roads where, now, no trace of a house remains.

Always makes me wonder who planted that tree. What has become of the people who lived in that house? Dead? Emigrated? What a thrill to discover the lilac tree still blooming bravely if they DID happen to come back?

Like the new Royal Court Hotel in Naas. Opened last week, it was fascinating for all of us who remember, particularly the Gardaí who served there when the place was the local Garda Barracks, to walk in and see what can be achieved when good taste is allied to money.

A magnificent old Georgian building, it would have been a desecration to pull it down – as, so easily, could have happened. Even the old stone coach house has been incorporated into the bar. What stories those walls could tell if stones could talk.

Whit Monday in five short days. Make no plans for the day other than a visit to the Irish Flowers Council's Floristry and Landscaping Spectacular at the Grand Hotel, Malahide.

I must say I am looking forward to my visit there and to meeting people who may have memories of "lilac days" when they were young.

If you watch Coronation Street on TV, you will understand how all that lilac talk has made my mind turn to a recipe for parsnip wine, which came into my hands some years ago and really does make a good brew.

Wash and slice four pounds of parsnips, pour on them six pints of boiling water, add 1½ ounces of ginger. Leave for four days to infuse (lovely word) and then to every gallon add two pounds of sugar, a half-pound of raisins, a half-pound of pearl barley and a half-ounce of yeast spread on toast.

Keep in a warm place and stir every day for about two to three weeks and then strain. Keep in barrel or other container until noise of fermentation (slight sizzling) stops. Then bung it into your container and leave it until you think it is mature.

Something else I've remembered. During the war, we used to make sandwiches of mashed parsnip flavoured with banana essence for visiting table tennis teams. No wonder we stopped under the lilacs on the way home!

(May 1991)

ON THE TREADMILL

If only we had been as wise ten years ago as we are today, how differently we would have planned our farming!

One thing sure and certain, that milking parlour out there in the yard would not have been built; indeed, the only milk used in this house would come from a bottle.

Now, with all that expensive equipment only half paid for, we are in up to our necks, and the people up in Merrion Street can do what they like with us. Our hands are tied, and short of winning the Sweep or dropping dead, there is no way of stepping off the treadmill.

Our foolishness in listening to all the people, who should have known better, advising us to get into milk and increase cow numbers has fashioned this big stick which is flaying us today.

The thing that depresses me most is the hopelessness of the situation – and the very last straw are the margarine advertisements on the television. These give me ulcers.

How they are countenanced in a dairy country like this mystifies me, but then so many things about present-day living do that.

Take shoes, for instance. I don't know how many women at last evening's ICA meeting agreed with my castigation of present-day shoes. Five different mothers had complaints about the bad workmanship in children's footwear and every woman present agreed about the difficulty of buying a shoe, for child or adult, which does not leak after a single wetting.

Now, Heaven's above, isn't this ridiculous? Men are walking on the moon, clothing which can insulate the human race from wind and cold has been invented, and yet they are making shoes which leak.

"We never guarantee these lightweight shoes as waterproof", the assistant in the big Dublin store told me when I brought back a pair of shoes Tom bought last time he was up for the Market.

"What do you mean, not guaranteed?", I asked. "Are you saying that, if a customer asks if these shoes are waterproof, you say they are not?"

"Well, they don't usually ask that", he answered uneasily, if honestly. I "created" about these shoes. It was not easy, and anyone might well be forgiven for giving up the battle in the light of the absolute non-co-operation of the assistant.

I had no intention of allowing myself to be browbeaten, however, and insisted on my rights. If all of us did this, it might make the manufacturers sit up and take more notice.

(June 1970)

JOYS OF JUNE

Only two days left of what was surely the most wonderful May ever as I write. Already my beloved hawthorn is faded and worn. Hurts to see it, but in a peculiar way it is reassuring.

Happens to everything and everyone, and any sensible being recognises this, but I still would love to cry "halt" and keep the young fresh beauty with us for that bit longer.

Ráméis? Of course! "Every dog", my father used to say, "has its day". And the hawthorn season of blossom is over.

From the wealth of blossom, there should be no scarcity of haws, and June, after all, with the morning air smelling of damp grass and earth, sparkling with sunlight and charged with the twittering of birds is standing in the wings, bedecked with roses, all ready to walk on stage.

Long past the stage in my life when loveliness is taken for granted, the beauty on our doorstep, so keen and direct that it is also poignant, brings with it a little stab at the heart.

Before we know it we shall be philosophising – fatal surrender for women for whom, being realists and materially-minded to boot, philosophy is apt to degenerate into a personal and selfish affair.

And being silage cutting time in this here household, there is no time for messin' as my offspring inelegantly dismiss any eulogies about the birds and bees.

The Marl Field, our first this year, was cut yesterday. Bare as a billiard table this morning, it is a far cry from the hay-making days of my youth.

I can still recall the sound of the horse-drawn mower as we walked home from the village school wondering as we came up the lane – cowslips and violets everywhere in the steep ditches – if they had held the pleasant job of bringing the tea out to the men in the field until we came.

Real joy that was! The "tommy" (a sweet bucket with a tight-fitting lid) full of strong, sweet tea swinging in one hand and a big round basket full of mugs and "cuts" of home-made soda bread smothered in freshly churned butter in the other.

Such a welcome there was from thirsty throats, and the men sat on the ground, a "sop" of hay under them, backs against the cock – or tram depending on where you came from – of hay and ate and drank to their hearts' content.

There was always a little mug for us included in the basket and you sat "filling your face" like the workers and listened to the "gostering" – a grand sound as soothing as a session of reflexology is, today.

Our local name for country chat, "gostering" in the hay field was usually about the progress – or not – of the neighbours.

We wondered what had delayed this one in coming out to "ruff-cock" his three acres that morning, or who had been responsible for the lop-sided trams in the field up on the brow.

Limited in range, maybe, because the talk never got beyond the confines of our own parish, but everything there interested us.

The reverse is in operation today. What is outside one's door is rarely noticed or discussed as people talk about faraway places seen on television – the invention that has transformed life for country people more than anything else in this past century.

When stock was discussed, all the breeds – few enough by comparison with today, come to think of it – were gone into.

The intricacies of the exact relationship required to fix the type of mountain stock in sheep without fear of softness through in-breeding, for instance, and often this extended to human genetics.

Unkind comments there were in plenty as well as kind ones. Who says the world – the people in it to be precise – have changed? They haven't at all!

(June 1990)

SICK FRIENDS

My mother came from Stoneybatter, down from what was then the Dublin Cattle Market in Prussia Street. My father, a horse-loving Wicklow farmer, up for the market, saw her crossing the street, considered that she had "good action" – stepped out well, in other words – and "got Kealy the cow buyer" (whoever he was) to introduce him.

For years, we came on periodic visits to my grandparents in Stoneybatter, a stern, elderly pair who believed firmly in the maxim that "children certainly should not be heard".

The trip up to the Big Smoke in those pre-electricity days was tremendously exciting. Not possessing a motor car, it began with Heuston Station (the Kingsbridge) and somehow or other Steevens Hospital across the road was invariably a focal point – for conversation and vision.

Mother had some story about a former, pregnant female owner of that hospital who, on seeing a beggar with a brood of children approaching the door for alms, instructed her servant to "remove that sow and her litter of bonhams".

Shocked to the core, because tramps were always treated courteously where we came from, we loved the sequel.

Cold-blooded, unfeeling little horrors (children haven't really changed, you know), reared on fairy tales of orphans being shoved into cages and fattened like the chickens in the coops in our own yard, it was always a matter of deep satisfaction to hear that, when the lady's own baby arrived, it had a pig's head!

Down the years, I've visited friends in Steevens Hospital and grown to love its courtyard and architecture – a replica of the beautiful Royal Hospital, Kilmainham.

Same feeling for the Richmond Hospital, Brunswick Street, with its handsome red-brick façade, and even good old Jervis Street, a place that has looked after cuts and bruises and broken limbs – and worse in so many cases – of staff from the *Independent*.

Sad to see all those old Dublin hospitals closing their doors. So much part of our history. Everything changes. We recognise that and eventually accept it, but it is not easy at the time.

Every family in the country has some connection with these hospitals, I feel.

(June 1987)

THAT SINKING FEELING

PSD – post-silage depression – was how the young man on the radio the other morning described the sinking feeling that assails many farmers at the present moment – realisation of the cost hitting them fairly and squarely in the solar plexus.

Afterwards, reading an article on "Efficiency in silage contracting" in a farming magazine with such emphasis on "careful planning to keep the harvester busy at every stage; to dovetail with the next job, avoiding any weak links like the plague and ensuring that knives are never blunt – because blunt knives will increase power requirement by up to 10pc", I felt a touch of PSD descending on myself. So difficult to see to everything! With the best will in the world, one falls down – at least it happens too frequently in this household.

Some farmers manage extraordinarily well – that tall Tullamore man, up for two days with a neighbour, had his first-cut safe and sealed, and top quality. We listened with envy, wondering how he does it, but it was reassuring talk and long may he continue to prosper is all the harm we wish him.

Maybe the weather wasn't as bad down his way? According to a friend, heavily into astronomy, Halley's Comet is responsible for the rain – the year of, the year before and the year after its appearance.

Bound to be bad weather. Shattering prospect! I refuse to believe it. Another old wife's tale, I'm certain.

Difficult to keep smiling, though. I do my best but that letter from an unfortunate small poultry-keeper in Owning, Carrick-on-Suir, makes my heart sink again. Such a sad tale, her small stock of pullets and ducks torn to pieces by dogs while she was away at a grandchild's Confirmation.

Arthritis keeps her from active farming but she loved her few hens and ducks and so enjoyed keeping neighbours in town supplied with free range eggs. Anyone got half a dozen Khaki Campbell ducks and a dozen laying pullets for sale, she wonders.

Interesting, isn't it, how the pendulum swings around! Five short years ago, the experts laughed when we lauded the flavour and nutritional value of free-range eggs and grass-reared chickens. Stupid to believe there was any difference, they assured us, but nowadays customers are prepared to pay extra – the ultimate test, when all is said and done – for the real thing.

Times must change, we all realise that, but what a pity so many mistakes are made in the process? Like the railways, for instance. We closed them "almost for sport", as the saying goes – and now realise the asset it would have been had some of these lines been left.

All the saving it would mean to roads – and to life and limb – and I'm sure the same will apply in a few years to the closure of County Hospitals. We shall live to regret it, without a doubt.

Delay in hay-making means no aftergrass for the calves. Nothing like a field of aftergrass free of parasites to "turn calves inside out". Our lot here are not thriving as well as we had hoped, so the concentrate (two to three pounds of rolled barley daily) has to supplement their meagre diet. Another disappointment, but the old-fashioned pink cabbage roses on the garden hedge are smelling as sweetly as they ever did. So it could be worse!

(June 1986)

PICNIC TIME

I am not, repeat NOT, griping about this beautiful sunshine, but working is not easy in this sort of weather.

We are dragging our legs about after us and most of us loath to complain. Rightly so!

Sunshine is precious and, come to think of it, if we got the chores done early in the morning or late in the evening and took a siesta at noon like they do in Spain, we would possibly be infinitely better off.

Trouble is getting down to that sort of living . . . and, more than probably, on the day we decide to do it, the rains would come.

Hard to decide which job I hate most – ironing with the sun beating down out of doors, or picking fruit. Both have their rewards.

That sense of satisfaction which a tall pile of ironed clothes gives any housewife. The row of glistening jars on the cupboard shelf, date neatly printed, that sends one to bed that night content.

Conscience is such a nuisance. One can't ignore the wretched thing all the time, just occasionally.

Like yesterday when, after deciding it was THE perfect day to paint the kitchen, men folk all away for the entire eight hours, I succumbed to temptation when a friend telephoned and asked if I would take advantage of the "massive day" that was in it and "take off" up the mountains with her on a picnic.

One tiny prick of feeling guilty was too weak to keep me on the straight and narrow.

Always a delight when someone else prepares a picnic. All I had to do was remove my painting garb (an ancient housecoat in which I like to imagine I look like an artist!) and I was ready for the off!

Waiting, I remembered as a child staying with a great aunt who, sensibly of course, believed in employing idle fingers, no matter how youthful they might be.

She asked me to dust the sittingroom and after a while, noting an interesting book in the fretwork-fronted bookcase, I took it out and got dug in. Some time later, she re-appeared and told me off, good and properly, for not finishing my work. "You must work first and play afterwards", she warned me, taking away the book – the title of which, astonishingly, I remember.

It was "Danesbury House" by a lady called Mrs Henry Woods, a moralist to the backbone, and later that night, my heart in my mouth in case I'd be caught, I stole downstairs and by the flickering light of a candle, dangerously close, I suppose to the bed-clothes, I read all about "flaring gin palaces" and the evils that come from frequenting such awful places.

Who knows? Maybe the incident is responsible for my distaste for the modern pub scene? No harm if that is the case – pub culture, unfortunately, is popular with too many today, old and young.

What a hypocrite I am, dismissing Mrs Woods as a moralist and I, the epitome of one myself?

"Don't do as I do, do as I tell you" – who was it said that, I wonder. Someone with more horse-sense than most, I feel.

The outing up the mountain was idyllic and the bare kitchen walls were still there when I came home. One great thing about housework – it will always wait.

(June 1989)

THE SCYTHE WAS KING

The scythe, long out of fashion, had never been moved from its hook, high up in the rafters of our farm workshop.

Well out of danger to curious children – and careless youth – it was a real operation taking the implement down to satisfy an elderly relative who, spying it, got the urge to mow the long grass in the orchard, in between gnarled stumps and, as we discovered subsequently, large rocks.

A curiosity these days, it was fascinating to watch an archaic bit of farming equipment in action after so many years.

Coat off, shirt-sleeves rolled up, Uncle Joe was delighted with his audience and kept up a running commentary on his days in the hayfields back in the Thirties when everything – and everyone – was pressed into service.

"We reckoned to mow the fur off the back of a sleeping mouse without waking it up", he told us with a twinkle in his eye.

And then the long story about how he and his brother had mowed a five-acre field in two days, a considerable feat on steep and rocky terrain.

Usual practice, it seems, was to get out at 5am, rest during the heat of the day and mow again in the evening. June must really have been June then, I thought.

The swish of steel on tall, almost-but-not-yet rank grass, swung me back to childhood. Such hard slogging work! Men – and water-carrying, washboard-rubbing women – were certainly fit in those days. How did they accomplish all they did, I wonder?

Suddenly, without warning, a clang as the scythe hit a cobblestone hidden in the grass. The whet stone available was obviously not much good. Uncle Joe tried.

Maybe he was tired but the job was abandoned and the scythe went back into retirement. When will it emerge again? Only the good Lord knows.

We are grateful for this temperate climate but it is difficult not to detest flies. They make so much extra work too, apart from the annoyance factor, and why do they attack one person quite viciously and ignore someone alongside? Can anyone enlighten me?

It has become a regular part of the morning's work for Tom, checking the sheep flock for cuts and scratches and treating these with antiseptic cream – a job he could well do without, but the flies are dangerous. Quite a bit of scouring among the calves too. The four on buckets were all affected and I refuse to believe hygiene was at fault – but the others on cows are in fine fettle, so I might be wrong.

At this moment as I look out the window, a flock of starlings descends on the fence. A flock? No, a gang, forty or more of the squawking, quarrelling marauders, out for the very last worm that can be dragged from the earth.

More than half, I notice, are babies, grey and woolly, already possessed of the typical starling manners, strutting about, being badgered here and there by mothers, bullying any other bird that dares to question their greedy supremacy. So much noise, not unlike what it was like with all those young foreign students on the top of the bus going out to Jurys Hotel one afternoon last week.

Young things, be it boys or girls, are noisy in groups, of course, come to think of it. Part of the process of growing up, I suppose. One should practice tolerance of all species. I must work on it.

(June 1990)

LONELINESS

Loneliness is a disease worse than any terminal illness. Like the lone pony in a paddock which pines without a mate (even a donkey to keep it company), where would we be without our friends?

Her face glowing with pleasure as she patted the simple little nosegay of garden flowers which a friend had brought in to cheer her up, the young woman in the hospital bed voiced the question that was on all our minds.

No, nothing in this world like friends, but do we show our appreciation enough, I often wonder? Alas, so many of us never do to all the carers around the country, who look after our elderly, incapacitated relatives.

Absolute dedication, taken for granted by siblings who actually often expect a visitor's welcome – high tea and trimmings – on the too rare occasions when they eventually get around to coming home to see a bed-ridden mother or father. Or even worse, someone in a world of their own, with that dreaded Alzheimer's.

Such a difficult disease to nurse. Constant unremitting vigilance required for the unfortunate (or should that be fortunate?) patient from the carer, who often has to cope single-handedly, not one hour of the day to call his or her own.

Can you imagine it? Doesn't bear thinking about – which is probably why we don't. No wonder the Western Alzheimer's Foundation in Claremorris, Co. Mayo, won a special award at the regional finals of the FÁS Community Initiative awards.

Thoroughly deserved recognition for this first-ever-in-Ireland Alzheimer's home support scheme where, these days – thanks largely to the initiative of the scheme director, John Grant, and his committee and FÁS, of course, which provides the funds – 108 people, who were literally prisoners in their own homes, are getting regular weekly breaks at last.

Another "bee in my bonnet" is the prodigious amount of work – unrecognised work – which community-minded folk put into organising their local shows.

Talk about being taken for granted! We should be on our knees in gratitude to these wonderful men and women who give so freely of their time, energy and expertise, for months on end beforehand. Shows like Kildare County Show in Athy don't just happen, you know.

Retaining a local show, without which our rural parishes would be even poorer than they already are, means long hours of hard slog and, human nature being what it is, we find thoughtless exhibitors, rarely in time with their entries, involving an impossible task for compilers of the catalogues – extra, unnecessary work for organisers.

A reader, just back from a holiday in Canada, was kind enough to enlighten us about a new cure for arthritis or, more correctly, relief from the scourge.

It is raisins (of all things) and gin. You need one box of golden (light) raisins (I got mine in the local health food shop, not cheap, but for relief, who cares?) which you pour into a shallow container. Pour enough gin (cheapest you can get) to completely cover the raisins.

Allow to stand uncovered, stirring occasionally to help evaporation, until all liquid disappears (about seven days). Place the raisins in a covered container and eat just nine (no more) daily.

(July 1996)

A FEAST OF COLOUR

Pansies – the garden is full of them and no flower I love more. Certainly, none give better service.

A blaze of colour for very small outlay, the spirit of eternal economy instilled into me by growing up in the Economic War of the Thirties which, sadly or happily (depending how you look at it), has never left me.

The portable window box of pansies on the kitchen window sill is my pride and joy.

Coming down to the empty kitchen quite early – who wants to stay in bed these beautiful mornings with the air smelling of dewy grass and earth, sparkling with sunlight? – there my pansies are, nodding good morning. And, sometimes, the extra thrill of a new one on the verge of opening.

Who could be lonely with a window box of pansies staring in at them?

You do know, I'm sure, that pansies always turn towards the house. No matter where you sow them, their little faces eventually turn housewards.

Fanciful? Maybe, but it's my story and I'm stickin' to it. I also believe the fairytale that, once upon a time, all pansies were white and it wasn't until one was struck by a bolt from mischievous Cupid's bow that it became stained with purple and endowed with magic properties for use in love philtres.

They are dedicated to St Valentine, by the way, and everyone knows that the pansy signifies thoughts. The name comes from the French *pensée*, a thought.

Facts, who wants 'em? Not I.

I prefer to keep on the fairytale track and remember the pea, shot casually from a boy's peashooter, that lodged on the window sill of a city tenement and grew there to the delight, and eventual cause of recovery from a wasting illness, of a young girl dying in that garret, to whom the growing green plant gave a reason for living.

Reason, by the way, for telling you that my window box of pansies is portable, thus enabling me to shift it from the window when the midday sun is too strong, is to stress the importance of taking care when bending.

I didn't yesterday and am paying for my stupidity with a stiff back.

So terribly easy to damage these "carcases" of ours and so many accidents, alas, could so easily have been avoided.

This time of year, with everyone going "hell for leather" at silage, spraying, etc., we are all guilty. All take too many chances with lethal things like electricity, high loads too close to power lines, flinging up those last few bales when you know in your heart the load already is too high, going helmetless for that pint of milk on your bike up to the shop on the corner, using an extension ladder without ensuring that the catch is in place.

The awful futility afterwards of reflecting on what we should – and could – have done. And, now, too late.

Holiday time with relatives and friends from towns and cities coming out for a day on the farm. God be with the days when this was no hassle, when drawing in the hay with the bogey and old grey mare was the big treat – and what bliss that was.

Do you remember sitting on the side of the bogey, the long aftergrass tickling your bare legs as you jogged across to pick up a cock – or tram – of hay.

It is just imagination to say there was no danger, but certainly nothing like today when the farm is a factory with danger on every side for the unwary small visitor.

(July 1992)

HOME FROM AMERICA

Tom's cousin Stephen, who emigrated to the States in his early twenties, is here with us on holiday. The two were great buddies in their youth and this reunion is a matter of extreme satisfaction to both, I am glad to see.

It so often happens that the reverse is the case, and I am always very sorry for people who find it impossible to bridge the gap which years and a totally different living environment often impose.

They sit up at night yarning away until the small hours and the occasional guffaws of laughter floating up the stairs indicate that they are reliving some of the mad schemes they were involved in together as boys when the pace was slower and "a fellow was counted lucky to have a bike with good tyres".

I was interested to hear Stephen's reminiscences about the farm as it was when he lived next door on the two hundred acres now occupied by three Mayo migrants. He feels a bit sad to see so many of the hedges gone and there was quite a lively argument between himself and Tom about the ultimate advantages of interfering, as he called it, so drastically with the balance of Nature.

He has a point too, I suppose. By removing hedges and trees, farmers have undoubtedly increased very considerably their productive acreage and made fields a better size and shape for the manoeuvrability of machinery.

With the ever-worsening labour shortage and bigger and bigger machines requiring more unimpeded field room, farmers have little alternative. Yet, even among this hard-headed fraternity, there are many unhappy at the loss of beauty in a well-loved landscape, stripped of its familiar hedges.

Too much resentment against change is not good however, and it is as well for the die-hards to remember that all these hedges were man-made not so very long ago either.

Nature, as has often been said, is the best plastic surgeon of all time and she can perform wonders in a short time to heal the wounds that even the most enormous bulldozer can do in an area.

Nobody, least of all farmers, advocates a hedgeless countryside. For hundreds of years, hedges have tamed fierce Spring gales, protecting the soil from ground winds that, untrammelled, can whip up and carry off thousands of tons of top soil that takes hundreds of years to replace, damaging tender young plants and stealing expensive fertiliser.

It is easy to wax sentimental about farm hedges, as American Stephen does, and just as easy for farmers like Tom to argue that hedges have served their purpose in a bygone age of husbandry and should now be erased from a countryside which can only progress with modern power farming.

Like so many things in life, wisdom lies between the two extremes.

(July 1970)

GREAT INVENTIONS

The wonderful works of a wheelbarrow – there was a joke in the village school disparaging this humble article. So long ago I disremember what exactly it was, but have you ever tried a gardening job that requires a bit of haulage WITHOUT a wheelbarrow?

"Bull's work" – as the blacksmith's wife described washing her husband's smoke-encrusted shirt in a wooden tub with a washboard – dragging earth or stones or whatever, from A to B on a sheet of plastic or lugging smaller amounts in a bucket.

Superb invention really, when you come to think of it, like the clothes-peg. Who was it, I wonder, invented clothes-pegs?

Clipping the open top of a cereal packet tight this morning with a clothes-peg, quite the fastest way of ensuring constant freshness – if you've never tried it, you are missing out – I saluted the genius behind clothes-pegs and wondered how any well-run household can manage without them

And, like so many other objects that have been tarted-up, the old-fashioned wooden variety is still streets ahead of its brightly-coloured attractive-looking plastic sister . . . a lesson or moral there somewhere, I'm sure.

The fifteenth of August already past. Has any year flown so quickly? No wonder the present unseasonable weather is creating panic in sun-loving hearts.

Interest in weather signs at the moment is a minor neurosis because we aren't resigned to the fact that it nearly always rains at this stage of the summer. But it is a day-to-day business and the thought nags us that, if today we sat out in the sun, it may have been the last time for weeks.

In autumn – and certainly in winter – we are resigned to what must be and thankful for the odd day or two of mellow sunshine.

Talk, on meeting, is always about the weather, the nearness or distance of the hills, the appearance of black slugs on the roadside verges and even the emergence of the common snail from below boulders and the nooks and crannies of stone walls, taking on a special significance when the weather charts on TV don't suit us.

A snail on the garden path this morning stopped me in my tracks and, childishly, I addressed it with the old chant: "Snail, snail a pooka, put out your four horns".

And what do you think, it obliged!

(August 1989)

SUNSHINE HABITS

Real sorry I feel for the unlucky holiday-makers who opted for holidaying out of Ireland this year. Would anyone in their senses want more sunshine than we've had this past week? I doubt it.

It was a chance, of course, as always. You win some, you lose some, but Ireland, when the weather is truly summery, is the greatest place on earth. Even the men of this household have become used to eating out of doors.

To date, it was always a "performance", persuading them to sit down and relax around the old metal garden table that held china plates, cups and saucers in Grandmother Carr's day, when the tennis court, now sadly no more, was in action and visitors arrived in ponies and traps.

Nowadays, it is usually mugs. Indeed, my friend Madeleine remarked the other day that this generation of young people may well be unaware of saucers, they are so infrequently used.

Interesting thought, as was the letter in the *Independent* one day last week about men "returning to savagery" by appearing everywhere, even at the dinner table, shirtless.

I couldn't agree more. The male torso close up, unless in the bed or the bathroom, is neither appealing or graceful, but the modern male obviously thinks differently.

Reaching across the table for the butter, not even a body like Adonis is palatable to my way of thinking, but then, I'm hopelessly old-fashioned, I suppose.

Hard to credit it is already autumn. Harvest is so much earlier that it was even ten years ago and the bare-swept fields are a wonderful old gold colour after the combine.

On the hill across from the house here, the four fields greening up after the last silage cut, are all different shades – rather like a patchwork quilt thrown over a tilted bed.

Overhead, the cumulus clouds of early autumn cast shadows across the bare fields, a sign of the shortening day and, down the canal, we gather giant bull-rushes for preserving.

Now is the time too to crush branch-ends of beech for dipping in their autumn solution of glycerine and water (equal parts). Perfect indoor decoration for the bleak days of winter, both.

The bull-rushes should be hung in a draught to dry and then paint the velvety parts of them with clear varnish which helps prevent them splitting.

The beech boughs go into a half-and-half solution of glycerine and water – a narrow-necked container like a milk bottle is ideal – and left to absorb the liquid.

Their lovely brown natural colour, like the bull-rushes, are nicest, I think, but the latter can be sprayed quite successfully if you want to match a colour scheme.

The coming Thursday is a special date in the diary. Down Offaly way, at Clara, the local development association has organised esker and bog guided tours. Too few of us regrettably know anything about the vital importance of bogs to our heritage so it is an important step.

"Clara Bog belongs to the world. We have a treasure there people will travel far and wide to see. One of the wonders of our natural world", is how David Bellamy describes it.

(August 1990)

MUSHROOMS

After the rain, we knew there would be mushrooms – and we were right. The Marl Field on Thursday evening was white with them and, like children at a party, we "made beasts of ourselves".

Marvellous experience, picking mushrooms. I suppose because they are a bonus harvest – something we get for nothing – and there is magic in the way they spring up overnight.

Early morning is the right time to pick mushrooms. Every country person worth his salt knows that but who can resist the temptation at any hour.

Real thrill, of course, is getting out there before anyone else, filling your basket up with "flats" and "buttons" and then coming indoors and doing a delicious cook-up for breakfast. Nothing tastier with a rasher, and nothing makes better soup than fresh field mushrooms.

"Up in the night, you'd get to eat it", for sure, and so simply made nowadays with the food-processor. In the old days, we put the cooked mixture of mushrooms and onions through a sieve.

A tiresome business by comparison with the blender, so we count our blessings and decide to make another supply tomorrow – and the day after – so long as there's a drop of rain to bring up the little wonders from the warm earth.

Food glorious food, perish the day when I shall lose interest in this absorbing topic.

Down at Tullow Show recently, we had a great chat over lunch about potatoes. The tasty helping we were masticating was probably accountable, but interestingly, everyone around the long trestle table agreed that there is no more appealing food, particularly when one is feeling "seedy".

Someone remarked that "there is a cure in the spud" and seemed surprised that I had never heard the saying before. Think back on family members and friends I have nursed in short and terminal illnesses down the years, potatoes and butter was an unfailing success when all else failed to tempt a capricious appetite.

"Pandy" we called the potatoes and farm butter we ate daily as young children. I am sure there are other names around the country for the dish that my generation was reared on – it would be nice to hear them.

Whatever about that, I sampled a new recipe for my repertoire and it was quite delicious. Plain boiled potatoes with a dressing of natural yoghurt, chopped parsley, chives, a crushed clove of garlic, salt and pepper. Really no end to the dishes which can be improved by the addition of yoghurt – chicken and lamb, for instance.

No mystery about doing so either. Clear concise directions in the National Dairy Council leaflets which are freely available.

Did you know there is as much protein – and first-class protein at that – in a five-ounce carton of yoghurt as there is in an ounce of meat or an egg, that the five ounces of yoghurt supplies about 10pc of the daily protein needs of an adult or 13pc for a child?

I confess I didn't, but I do believe that with the alarmingly high incidence of osteoporosis (brittle bone disease) – about every other woman I know seems to be suffering from it – it is vitally important that we all, young and not so young females, ensure that we get enough calcium.

In my own bones, I feel that all the concentration on slimming which caused so many young women to give up milk completely is largely responsible for the amount of brittle bones about.

I know it's important to be slim and trim and obesity is a curse, but overdoing it with regard to forgetting the daily calcium requirement is extremely foolish.

(August 1990)

SEASON OF FRUIT TREES

The subtle change as the sun creeps back imperceptibly towards the horizon, its angle decreasing a little every day, means autumn.

Another indication, absence of bird-song. Suddenly the silence is noticeable, although when exactly the chorus begins to diminish, I never quite know.

All at once though, it is the sad plaintive twittering of the wren, the very occasional tentative few bars of some small bird deep in the leaves of the sycamore, or high on some bush, where I never manage to spot it before it is silent again, that makes me aware that something is no longer there.

I like this time of year myself. More energy for work and there is the satisfaction of hedgerow "scavenging" – getting material for the table and the store cupboard for nothing – mushrooms popping up everywhere after a few hours of sunshine, blackberries on the edge of ripeness and elderberries for jam, jelly and wine.

Guess the people I feel most sorry for at this time of the year? Pupils and teachers, back to the grind after the over-long – for both sections – holidays.

Why do I sympathise so much? Long, long years after all since I faced the dreaded return to the village school after a magic summer of sunshine, bogey rides, "babby house" games in the thick shrubbery of the garden ditch, strawberries, red dessert gooseberries which we simply called hairy, home-made jam on "cuts" of soda bread, sitting in the swing longing for a push.

Remember all the marvellous "messin' about" of childhood when, really, the only important thing in your life was freedom.

Yes, oddly, in spite of lost contact, the memories come crowding back at this time of the year, even though I know that modern children get bored easier than we did.

Indeed, many welcome the resumption of the school year, I believe, with all this new technology, computers, language laboratories and the team games in which the majority revel. Being a coward, I never did. I imagine there are lots of youngsters enduring this week the same stomach knots.

Teachers too! The problem of controlling present day children, many hopelessly spoiled by over-indulgent parents, must be enormous.

No other word for it! All so knowledgeable about their rights, daring teachers in many cases, aware that no finger can be laid on them no matter how unruly their behaviour.

Walking myself into a hornet's nest of criticism, I know, when I assert that the odd slap never did a child any harm. Highly unpopular it will make me with friends who feel strongly about corporal punishment, violence begetting violence, etc., etc.

Quite right too! There were sadist teachers in my day and, for all I know, some still exist – a shocking thought.

And those of us with healthy children are so lucky. Too many for whom the reverse, alas, is the case.

(August 1989)

HARVEST OF THE BINDER

Like great grey and red hippopotami, the two combines browsed slowly through the forty-acre field of barley and, strangely, the hum of the engines from the distance reminded me of a totally different harvest era.

In the binder days, the harvest often took a month – or six weeks, or even two months, according to the weather. So many hazards which could hold things up. Laid corn was, perhaps, the most common problem.

In our part of the world, July so often brought a lot of wind and rain that would come sweeping across the sea and would wreak havoc on the tallish corn which was mostly the crop sown on our hill-farm.

You'd go to bed at night leaving a fine upstanding field of corn and, in the morning, you'd find it flattened and twisted all ways as if some demonic giant had been laying about him with a flail.

And laid corn made things more than usually difficult for the binder, especially a temperamental and ancient model like ours.

If the field was one of the steep ones, we often had to cut one way, driving into the head of the corn as it lay on the ground, then driving back idle before going for another bite in the same direction.

Thinking back, I wonder how we ever managed to harvest at all in some of those appalling Augusts and Septembers of the war years.

I suppose we just kept on cutting even when it wasn't ripe and, frequently, with the dew still on it, hoping against hope that it would ripen in the stook.

Sometimes it did but more often it didn't and we'd be out there turning the sheaves to stop them sprouting, inside and out and back again, hard hand-work all the time and, oh, those thistles.

Messing about with wet sheaves was guaranteed to wet you to the skin. And no plastic either! The men used to tie hessian sacks around their waists which made the work even harder, struggling on and on under the extra weight.

A great problem in those days was the length of the straw. Spraying with chemicals was unheard of and sometimes wheat straw could be four feet long.

Drawing in the crop was another major headache. Bogeys, carts, everything pressed into service and, unlike the drawing of the hay and the pleasure of bogey rides, the "thistley" corn and the sharp stubble underfoot, often full of water that squirted up and soaked bare legs and sandals, was something we shunned.

Sheds were scarce too and mostly the corn was built into ricks and these had to be thatched as soon as possible to keep out the wet.

It was a good feeling when the haggarts were eventually occupied, the giant ricks changing the familiar scene and making the place perfect for games of "tig" and for housing the family sheepdog, usually in a tar barrel tucked cosily into the base of a rick.

We have so much for which to be grateful in this country. Looking out at the wonder of green grass after the burnt countryside of ten days ago makes one count one's blessings. It takes so little to bring on grass here in Ireland.

Ninety-five degrees in Kennedy Airport yesterday when relatives returned there, after two weeks here, and the air-conditioning out of action, to boot.

So they told us when they telephoned bang in the middle of a thunderstorm, the rain pelting down into the thirsty lawn field as I listened to voices four thousand miles distant.

(August 1989)

ACCIDENTS

Accompanying a friend to the out-patients of a country hospital last week, I was horrified by the condition of a young man linked in by two mates after a chain-saw accident. Scalped almost, and all because he was not wearing a helmet.

I was particularly upset because only a few hours earlier I had checked out a fifteen-year-old neighbour who was waving a chain-saw about as he chatted with a couple of equally feckless teenagers.

God help them but they haven't a "stim" of sense and, unfortunately, the same often applies to their elders, who often pay insufficient attention to the carelessness of youth, allowing sons and daughters to take off on big machinery without a fear in the world.

You know yourself, I'm sure. Hidden gateways and a tractor driving out at speed, or watching a schoolboy tearing down a slope with a trailer behind. No thought for what could happen.

"You can't put an old head on young shoulders". We all recognise that but it doesn't help when you are waiting, heart in your mouth, in a hospital to hear just how badly some young worker has been injured.

Accidents are so appallingly easy to "come by". Waiting around every corner for us, every hour of the day, but yet, we all feel, most especially youth, that it can't happen to us.

Preaching is a waste of time. How well I recognise that, but one has a duty to speak out at times and too many farmers (of necessity, I know) allow youngsters to operate machinery too powerful for inexperienced drivers.

Modern tools are marvellously efficient by comparison with the laborious slog of my young days when people spent hours scything grass and trimming hedges. I still enjoy a short spell of the latter – when the lawn shears are sharp and I don't have to over-reach myself.

I recall vividly the enormous sense of achievement it gave me many years ago when I crenellated an old hedge in the garden. It was the feeling of having personally altered the landscape, I think, apart altogether from the achievement of having turned a dull piece of garden screening into something of delight.

We still have a scythe hanging in the shed and I often find myself stroking it as I pass. Summer days of yesteryear, there always was the swish of grass falling under the scythe blade, the keenness of which was achieved with a sharpening stone or "strickle".

Usually that same article was missing when the Boss decided to sharpen the scythe but, once found, it always was soothing to stand and watch the Master at work as he honed and honed until the requisite keenness was achieved.

And all the while, there would be talk. Tales of what it was like in his young days when "men were men" and the ambition was "to mow the fur off the back of a sleeping mouse without wakening it".

Also how important it was to take up a comfortable stance. “Heel down, point up” was the first rule of scything, and the frustration, when after all his work getting the requisite razor edge, tall grass and cocksfoot heads falling rhythmically under the blade, without warning the sudden clang telling of iron against stone, and the culprit, a round smooth cobblestone hidden in the grass and catching the scythe heel, sometimes almost buckling the point.

(August 1993)

BLOSSOMING FORTH

Five or so years ago, when daughter Maura was "madly in love" with a young horticultural student, he gave her an apple tree.

Nice gesture, and nothing would do her but to plant it smack in front of the sittingroom window – "so that we could admire the blossom in spring".

The idea was pleasant, but it didn't work out. The tree grew too big and, in this house, the oldies like light.

That particular boyfriend has long gone out of the daughter's life and nowadays she is at home so seldom, and notices so little anyway, that it matters little about the spring blossom, so we moved the tree.

Tom felt it was a waste of time bothering too much, but a tree is a tree, so we dug a big hole and stuck it into that bit of waste ground across from the old hen-run, a place we rarely have reason to visit.

Occasionally I noted its progress, which wasn't great, and had forgotten about it until something – what I don't know – brought me across to look at it one night to see, unbelievably, a perfect pink blossom on one of its shrivelled boughs.

Magic sight that surprisingly appealed to that most unsentimental and uneasily impressed of mortals – Tom Carr.

He stood for a good ten minutes staring at the miracle and, when our Murphy neighbours arrived up after dark for the whist game, what do you think?

Before the cards were produced, Ned Murphy was brought out to see the blossom by the light of a flashlamp.

Afterwards, over the rubber (love that word – always reminds me of post-threshing evenings when someone was always bound to suggest a rubber), we all threw in our tuppence worth of thoughts about the tree.

Everyone, of course, wanted the tree to thrive and produce apples, that goes without saying, but someone (female, I may say) felt that solitary blossom might just be a final gesture, a sign before death, its private flag to remind this household that, had they paid more care, it would have repaid us a thousand-fold.

Gave us food for thought – and conversation – which as always was of things rural, the swift march of time (that applies to all, of course) the way the robin sings so much at this time of year, and the beauty of these early autumn mornings with the flowers that are left, shining with colour out of the grey mists, and bushes and shrubs draped with dewy gossamer.

Someone recalled (inevitably at this time of the year) the October threshings of the Forties and Fifties, odd things like corn-carrying, that gave men with sixteen-stone sacks on their backs a stately walk and ability to hump it "up steps" a higher rank in the rural hierarchy.

Someone mentioned elderberries. It is a good year, with glossy bunches of them hanging down to nose-level along the over-grown bridle path to the ancient graveyard – long closed for burials.

We all make elderberry wine down here and last year's was drunk and commented on as the cards were dealt. But few make elderberry jam or jelly. The former requires six pounds of ripe berries, four pounds of sugar, one tablespoon orange-flower water.

Put the berries in a preserving pan with barely enough water to cover. Heat until fruit is soft, a few minutes; add the sugar and orange-flower water and cook for 45 minutes, stirring and skimming. Test as for all jams and pot as usual.

(September 1988)

A FOUR-LEGGED PEST

For some unknown reason, our parlour chimney is a sounding-board for dogs barking.

Only when the fires burn low, those precious minutes that you get too infrequently, when the family has gone to bed and you have time to sit and stare into the dying, glowing embers.

Far away it always sounds, as if it were coming from a dog away down in the valley, and never – irritatingly, endlessly and idiotically – like the dog that keeps you awake at night.

A comforting, nostalgic sound I always feel that brings back the past, redolent of flickering paraffin yard-lamps, of cosy byres, of pre-intensive dairying days.

Or the soothing noise of adults "gostering" about prices of stock at fairs, the brightness of the stars on clear nights, how the hens had "gone back" with egg production – and then the sudden rush of air when the back door was pushed open by a caller (or, as we used to call them, mitcher) in for a game of 25, perhaps.

While, from the comfort of his half-boarded wooden barrel under the rick, the family collie barked dutifully, indicating that he was doing his duty, warning us of the arrival.

A dog barking throughout the night, keeping people awake, has become a real pest in towns, I'm told.

Generally, a barking dog is an ill-kept dog. Too many householders, who are neither equipped nor committed enough, decide to keep a dog without giving the business sufficient thought.

Result is neglect – and in a sheep district, often disaster. Any dog will sleep, if it is caninely possible. This is not possible if he is hungry, wet, cold, dirty or tormented by parasites.

How often have you seen dogs housed in a cheerless draughty barn or bedded down on a pile of superannuated sacks, invariably damp, seldom changed?

Such a dog will bark remorselessly once he gets started and the unfortunate light sleeper – maybe ill and longing for a few hours peace – will toss and turn and think longingly (and who can blame him?) of remedies like a gun or poison.

Which my neighbour did last night when five of her laying hens were whipped by Master Reynard. Felt so sorry for her in the yard this morning when she poured out her sad tale.

Grand hens they had been too and just once – which was once too often – the catch of the door had been carelessly latched.

My own immediate world looks different this morning after the road hedge, for a full mile down, has been cut. The hedge-cutter spent yesterday roaring and grunting and grazing off the top two-thirds like some primeval monster.

And recognising the necessity of machines to do this job – because the responsible workmanship, experience and what Masefield called "skill and sense of strength of arm" have been priced out of consideration. I hate hedge-cutters.

Ruthless and uncaring for wildlife, or indeed the future value of the hedge they are murdering, they organise the new growth shoot straight upwards, ensuring that stock will walk through the invariable gaps in a year or two. Barbed wire will then be used to plug the holes – barbed wire, the indication of the deficiencies of modern farming.

Plenty of technology, plenty of money – but neither can replace the good human hand and eye when it comes to stockmanship and craftsmanship.

(September 1989)

COUNTING THE PENNIES

Only natural that we should have been hoping for similar prices to last year for our lambs. Optimism is ever-present in the human heart, even if we know, deep down, that last year's prices were "over the top" as George Rothwell of Bagenalstown Ewe Breeders said at their sale the other day. Prices this year are "more realistic", he believes.

Disappointing, of course. That cash had already been spent and now we have, as grandfather used to say, to "draw in our horns". Heaven knows money is tight enough. The stuff, as always, come to think of it, seems to melt.

Wheeling the trolley up to the cash-out in the supermarket, after casting a quick eye and then making a mental note of how much one has in one's purse, I find many others joining me in rejecting items, abandoning them on the approach stretch.

Often strikes me how much supermarket personnel must hate that. Jars of coffee among the breakfast cereals, soap alongside the pearl barley – I can just imagine what they must mutter under their breath.

Before leaving pearl barley, I must just remind you how wonderfully good that particular commodity is for backache. A friend recalled this during the week when I brought up the subject of aching backs.

No sympathy for anyone who doesn't use pearl barley, she barked at me, and sure enough it was an invaluable remedy in the good old days of the black range when a saucepan of pearl barley was always simmering away for farmers who then, as now, were unhappily so prone to the curse of backache.

Barley water is great for the complexion too, incidentally, a great "cure-all" you could call it. We don't use it much nowadays because it requires long slow cooking and is too much trouble.

Trouble! Do modern housewives know the meaning of that word by comparison with their mothers and grandmothers? I doubt it – and yet here I am who remembers well, writing stupid things like the "good old days of the black range".

Hateful thing that same range, the bane of our lives, impossible to regulate, with an insatiable appetite for fuel and a vast expanse of surface for weekly black leading. Sometimes I honestly think nostalgia is a disease worse than rheumatism.

Apropos which, yet another old-time remedy for that very complaint in faded pencil on the back page of Grandmother Carr's old recipe book.

The brown paper cover had it hidden from view until some inquisitive fingers unearthed it during the past week. I am compelled to pass it on.

Before doing so, hands up any of you who remember the great business it was covering new school books every year with stout brown paper? Compulsory it was in the village school and woe betide you for "showing off" if you had succumbed to the temptation of using "fancy" wallpaper – bits left over from the parlour's annual face lift.

Very simple, this particular recipe. You need an ounce each of cream of tartar, epsom salts, ginger, bread soda and sulphur. Mix all thoroughly and take half a teaspoon in half a glass of warm water every night.

(September 1989)

TREMENDOUS SHOCK

"Than these September skies is no sky lovelier" – a line from a poem dredged up from schooldays and misquoted. It was November skies they were talking about – but the description applied perfectly to the scene as I drove home from the village last evening, the week's groceries in the boot of the car.

Low down, in front, almost on the horizon, swirls of pearly grey. A luminous grey with nothing foreboding about it, for all the world like a chiffon evening dress dropped on the bedroom floor by one of these debut-going teenagers (what a lot of rot all that is) and on my right, in contrast, brilliance – pink streaks on a blue and turquoise background, a sight that injected brightness and optimism into my very soul.

A precious few minutes which I needed when I arrived home and found that Tom had trimmed the five cypress trees across from my kitchen window. Had I suspected that he had this job in mind before I left home, the groceries – even if they starved – could have waited.

Experience has taught me that men – the kindest, most likeable of them – can rarely be trusted with a trimming job. Seems that when they get a sharp instrument into their hands, unsupervised, they go berserk.

My precious five cypresses a perfect shelter belt, admittedly in need of having some overhanging branches cut back, were like five badly plucked fowl . . . scarified.

Not a branch left anywhere along the trunks, just tufts of green on top, rather like the old-time schoolboys' haircut – a bit left for the irascible schoolmaster to grab, if by some chance he'd got out of bed that morning on the wrong side, or his pony had cast a shoe.

Two of the calves had developed hoose, too. A real misfortune this to Tom, who genuinely couldn't understand all the fuss I made about the cypresses.

He got on with the calf-dosing and afterwards we'd both relaxed sufficiently to discuss (amiably enough, too) how we could make the two days of next week's ploughing championship in Tullamore.

Has time ever gone so quickly? Seems only yesterday when the dates and venue for the All-Ireland Ploughing Championships were announced, back at the start of the Summer, and now here we are, all set for Tullamore on Wednesday and Thursday.

As always, I'm looking forward to the annual expedition. Special in my calendar, marvellous altogether, if the weather is kind as it was last year – when we had that pleasant chat with a bishop whom I mistook for a rather shabby curate. A cleric with first generation farming blood flowing strongly in his veins, he fitted into the scene, standing there on the headland with the gulls screaming and whirling on the upturned earth behind the plough.

(September 1987)

DOWN FROM DUBLIN

"All that work with sheep", said my cousin from Dublin, down with us for a few days' peace and quiet after a spell of hospitalisation.

They were dosing the flock for worms and, with the collecting yard right under her bedroom window, she had had precious little rest that morning. Politely, however, she had assured me, when I apologetically "landed in" with her breakfast tray an hour earlier than intended, the operation viewed from her bed had been so interesting that she had not grudged the sleep.

Grandfather and Tom, dirty and smelling strongly of sheep, were delighted at her appreciation of the amount of work the job had involved when she came downstairs later on. They talked at length and most knowledgeably, I noted with secret amusement, of the right and wrong ways of dosing and there were many slighting references to sheep farmers who do not take enough care with administering the exact dose.

Being a strong believer in the policy of keeping family "face" intact before strangers – even blood-relations like cousins – I was careful to keep the smile on the side of my face turned away from my menfolk.

Until recently these same pair of Buckoes had been as sea-happy as the next about the dosing. Details like directions were considered utterly superfluous reading matter but, now that they have turned over a new leaf, the mote in the other fellow's eye is as big as an elephant.

A survey done by a pharmaceutical house in England, and passed on to them "for Gospel" by Ned Murphy's brother, one of the people involved, was responsible for the transformation.

It was discovered that the actual dose being administered varied from less than 2ml to nearly 10, the required amount being just below 4ml. This means, of course that the dose may have been, if not lethal, at least detrimental to health, and at the other extreme, too low to be effective.

In all cases, guns were used but the errors were not the fault of the instrument. They were due to a lack of regular checks, or calibrations as Ned's scientific-minded brother put it. It seems, by the way, that it is not difficult to do this yourself, with a standard glass measure for comparison.

Obviously, a few minutes and a few shillings spent in testing can save a lot of expense.

As Grandfather so wisely put it to my very impressed cousin: "Giving an overdose to a few hundred sheep can cost a fair amount of money, while giving an inadequate dose is a waste of time and money".

(October 1970)

A LITTLE RAIN

A momentary lull in the conversation of the tea table and my hostess and I gazed out at the rain.

"First time this year I've had to hook up the clothes line here", she announced, turning her glance upwards to where a couple of pairs of jeans and several socks dried in the warm air that wafted up from the old, but highly efficient, Aga cooker underneath.

Hard to credit, after all the rain of the past week, there is still a water shortage. It is a fact, however, and anyone who doubts should drive down to Blessington where the lake continues to sport at least twenty feet of dried-up vegetation around its entire circumference.

Conservation of water is still required and I make no apology for repetition. There must be no waste. Hopefully, at this stage, everyone with a suitable drainpipe has some sort of receptacle underneath.

Apart from the saving angle, there is nothing better for the hair – or face-washing – than rain water.

Soothing sometimes looking out at the rain – when you are nice and comfortable indoors, of course with no inclination to stir out. I like the sound of rain falling too – gentle, unlike the awful noise that surrounds us today.

It is not generally realised how dangerous noise can be. It can actually make people physically ill.

Among the complaints it causes are heart and circulatory diseases, chronic insomnia, lack of concentration, over-tasking of the nervous system and even high blood pressure.

Medical research has shown too that deafness can, in many cases, be attributed to noise and our young people, subjected to noise of their own making – from the appalling high level of music or what passes as music in their discos – are already suffering in varying degrees.

Noise is a waste product of modern civilisation and, in the euphoria of progress, while considered a nuisance, it is accepted as inevitable.

Until comparatively recently, that is. Much more is known now about the damage which transport giants can do – mammoth tankers at sea, "jumbo" airliners overhead and, nearer home, enormous lorries travelling at speed along roads that were never made to take such traffic.

We got our priorities wrong there, as well as in may other things, I'm afraid.

Too few of the planners thought of the effects of a motorway on the countryside.

For instance, did you know that a motorway on an embankment running across the flood plain of a river can act as a dam, while a motorway in a cutting can lower the water table of the surrounding area, killing trees. Noise from a motorway on the level or an embankment can travel a full mile unless screened by trees.

Life beside a busy motorway can prove intolerable with the engine noise and vibrations from heavy lorries. The very foundations of houses are weakened and, while large items of transport are, presumably, more economic, surely they lose flexibility.

We have grown accustomed to the effect of electricity pylons striding across the countryside – and those of us who can remember life before they came accept them cheerfully, but now there are gas and oil pipelines as well – all of which are forms of transport.

There is a tendency for transport to dominate the scene and yet, theoretically, transport is a service.

A service is something which serves, surely, and not something that dictates. Transport is for the benefit of mankind, not for oppression.

(October 1990)

A crisp October morning with a nip in the air and the tree tops emerging through the mists in the valley. On our way up to watch the men get that dead beech on the Churchyard Field ditch down at last, I was struck, as always, by something I feel is the essence of autumn – its scents.

Something which is true of every season, if one has the nose for it, and scents mean much. But somehow the mild damps of autumn are particularly favourable to scents, especially the rich, pungent smell of decaying foliage.

The scent of the ivy growing all over the trunks and branches of a whole line of trees down the lane was sickly sweet. Astonishing the assortment of insects attracted by the ivy. I noticed bluebottles and wasps and even a few bees lumbering about, with velvety coats that were tempting to stroke.

The ivy grows stronger on the ailing trees, rising in billowing folds of glossy foliage surmounted by countless umbels of green blossom. Lovely sight, but the extra wind leverage imposed on its host tree will eventually bring the whole shoot crashing down and nothing is more dangerous.

Diseased trees are a terrible menace on roadsides and no harm reminding readers of the responsibility they have to ensure that any tree which constitutes a danger to road users should be cut down.

The beech our men were cutting down, somehow or other, in spite of the ropes, fell awkwardly, missing the, admittedly old, but very useful cattle shed underneath by only a few feet.

It broke up on impact, a blessing for sawing and, as always, the thought of a supply of dry logs for the winter was reassuring.

Two schools of thought about ivy on trees. My friend Madeleine – quite an expert she is, too – feels passionately that we should all be out pulling the stuff off the trees. A task that might well keep youngsters out of mischief.

But Grandmother Carr's old diary has an entry on ivy in which she asserts, almost as vigorously as Madeleine, that "ivy flourishes only on trees that are already unhealthy. A strong tree's dense canopy of foliage is too umbrageous for an ivy to get the best out of life", she records in her spidery handwriting.

I've also read somewhere that, in a forest products yard in Montgomeryshire where tent pegs are made from ash, ivy is actually encouraged to grow on ash trees to prevent any branches below the crown from breaking out, thus giving the knot-free timber for this highly-specialised craft.

Those of us interested in growing trees could well find out the effect of ivy on trees at some of the Teagasc and Forest Training Service special short training courses.

Geared towards people growing trees commercially, all aspects of maintenance and management will be gone into with lectures, discussions and demonstrations. Keep your eye out for notices of them in the papers.

Comforting isn't it to find large bodies remembering hard-working past officials. The IFA down Limerick way, for instance, is making a determined drive to commemorate the late Paddy Fitzgerald, who did so much for the organisation in the early days.

(October 1992)

GRANDFATHER'S PENKNIFE

Grandfather has lost his penknife, a catastrophe which has the entire household in turmoil.

Heaven knows it was not worth much, monetarily speaking. Less than five shillings in the village shop twenty years ago, its hinge was as full of play as a sally switch, and its blade worn to a narrow quarter-inch strip of metal by daily, often indeed twice daily, honing on the old grind-stone in the yard.

A relic of another age, Grandfather, the only person to use this stone, refuses to allow its removal to a more inconspicuous corner. A nuisance in this day of swift vehicle-turning and reversing, it may possibly get knocked over, but personally, although I grumble occasionally, I would hate to see anything happen to it.

I feel that it provides the same safety valve in moments of frustration to my father-in-law as pop records do for Sean, or a long, hard walk does for myself.

The knife disappeared after it had been lent to that same careless young devil of a son of ours to trim a ewe's foot. Hours of long searching proved fruitless, and now poor old Grandfather has the discomfort of getting used to a new one. A fine-looking substitute, I must admit, it cost Sean more than he could afford and, being young, he cannot understand why his Grandfather should continue cribbing.

I point out as patiently as I can that the lost knife had the attachment that stems from daily use and, as such, was beyond value, but from the blank look on my offspring's face I know that it is a waste of time.

Maybe he cannot be expected to understand something which only comes with time. I sympathise in this instance, because I happen to have a similar knife among my kitchen equipment with which I would not part for diamonds.

A thin-bladed specimen which collects stains as quickly as an open pot of honey does flies, I bought it with a heap of junk at an auction when the "Big House" came under the hammer ten years ago, and I am sure that it must be at least 100 years old. It is the first item I see when I open the knife drawer, and the first tool I select for all jobs from slicing meat for a stew to cutting turnips.

Sharp as a razor, it does all that I ask of it effortlessly, and I have often thought that if I had known the value it was to prove to me, I would have cheerfully paid five pounds instead of the five shillings I handed over to the auctioneer's clerk in that old kitchen one April morning so many years ago, cursing myself at the time for a fool at being stuck with a pile of rubbish.

(December 1969)

SALTY BACON

A Kildare reader chides me gently for my pessimism in quoting the old saying about an abundance of haws indicating a hard winter ahead.

She reminds me: "A haw year is a braw year", and "a sloe year is a woe year".

"Chides me gently" – I stop typing and look at the three words and am reminded of "Sunday Readings for the Young" we borrowed from Church of Ireland neighbours. Full of morals and Sunday School teachers who were "young and pretty" and rarely "scolded" – just "chided" their little pupils, "gently, in soft voices".

Envied those same pupils we did, when our village schoolmistress actually caned us for missing afternoon devotions on Sunday.

I can remember imploring my father not to go visiting cousins in the next parish (a routine affair, but pleasant except when the Madeira cake for tea was caraway) on "Devotions Sunday", knowing what I would get on the Monday morning.

He paid no attention and the following afternoon if he happened to be picking us up in the pony and trap from the village school, we knew better than to whine about the two slaps we had received for non-attendance in church the day before.

Rancour? Do I hold any rancour in my heart for him today? Not an iota! Taught us to stand on our own two feet, injected that necessary length of iron into our spines, something sadly lacking in the upbringing of youngsters today.

Modern parents are too soft with their offspring. Children need preparing for the “slings and arrows” of this world – even the loftiest topple, as witness our political scene of recent days – not to mention the Iron Lady with the stony face as she sits listening to the ranting and raving against her in the British House of Commons.

I wonder if anyone enjoys watching television from there as much as I do? Infinitely better than any “soap” to my way of thinking.

Flicking through an ancient Carr family diary, I noted that the latter end of November was always pig-killing time here.

St Martin’s Day, November 11, is well and truly gone for this year, but that was the start of a job that went on in most farmhouses of the parish until the end of the month.

Timed to ensure a perfectly cured ham for Christmas maybe, although it was the weather that actually dictated, I suppose. There was no refrigeration, no electricity, so the pig was cured in brine in barrels, the hams smoked in the barn-chimney hanging from hooks way up in the grimy (I’m sure) soot-encrusted walls.

Twenty-four hours steeping to get the salt out was always required. Inedible otherwise, but it was great eating with floury potatoes and “bolsters” of green cabbage.

Amazing to think what a countrywoman could make out of one average-sized pig sixty years ago.

Pork in every guise, from pies to delicious pork steaks, the head boiled down to make brawn or, as we called it, "collared head", black pudding made from the freshly-caught blood with oatmeal and onions, and "leaf" lard rendered down to make delectable fried bread for breakfast before school that I can still taste mentally. Scrumptious with a fresh, free-range egg.

Food for all the kings in the world and no worry then about being overweight. We walked off any excess and even those who didn't never worried.

Fine big men and women were admired then, even envied. How the world has changed.

(November 1990)

BULLS AND WRENS

The curly-haired neighbouring dairy farmer was finishing his tea before sallying forth into the chill December evening to milk, when I called for the parish collection.

Strong, white teeth bit into a "cut" of home-made bread and he took a final gulp of tea before giving me his full attention.

"That Larry O'Loughlin guy knew what he was talking about when he told you about never trusting a bull", he remarked.

For a moment I was at sea, until I remembered a diary which dealt with that seminar on farm accidents run by Teagasc.

"Why so?" I enquired.

"Well", he said, leaning down to pull on the muddy Wellingtons on the step outside, "we were down driving in fencing posts today and my bull, normally quiet as a dog, came across to a pile of plastic sacks we'd taken off the electric fence and to say he 'malavogued' them is putting it mildly".

Tough man, Michael, normally, not easily upset, but this incident had undoubtedly frightened him. It was good, I thought, to hear a man admit what, possibly, he would consider weakness.

Hopefully, someone out there will benefit, and treat the farm bull, familiar though they may be with him, cautiously at all times.

From the sublime to the ridiculous, except that bulls ARE not sublime and wrens are not ridiculous.

Looking out from the bedroom window this morning, I spotted one hunting as busily as any hungry bird I have ever seen.

At first I thought it was a mouse. There is a resemblance, don't you think?

This one was certainly mouse-like, as it darted from the cover of some dead stalks at the side of the wall, examining crevices in limestone, popping into holes hardly big enough to admit the tiny body and out again just as quickly.

An overhang of dead vegetation, sepia, withered, waiting for spring, provided an untidy curtain, then out again the other side before darting off to the comparative security of the gnarled old thorn which is also so full of knots and holes that I lost it from sight.

Strangely independent little creatures, they seem to pay less attention to their neighbours than almost any other species.

Hunting as they do, they must often run into trouble from creatures similarly engaged, stoats, rats, weasels that also search the dead stalks, the heaps of old dead leaves and the debris that accumulates in the corners of gardens and farmyards.

The death toll among wrens is obviously high but they lay a large number of eggs and I recall seeing fledglings emerge from their domed home one spring in such a procession that I could scarcely believe it when the last one left and there were no more to come.

Of course, they get enormous hassle during nest-building time. A nest, painstakingly built, is often abandoned after a few days, the occupants driven away by plundering mice or bird-nesting youngsters.

But the wrens struggle, until eventually a brood is brought out . . . a lesson for many of us there.

(December 1992)

MARTHA'S PASSING

Changes everywhere, but at least the traditions of Christmas – mixing the pudding, icing the cake – retain a reassuring familiarity.

Time was when these two weeks were a whirl of poultry preparation, killing, plucking and delivering the forty or so turkeys we had so painstakingly reared for the previous six months to the extent, unbelievably now when I look back, of pulling nettles and chopping them fine as parsley for the finicky young poultry.

There was even an era of hard-boiled egg feeding – and rice – which you fed squatting on your "hunkers" from a wooden paddle, carefully ensuring that weaker, timid birds got their share.

For all that trouble, we might get the magnificent price of 2/6 per lb – twelve and a half pence in today's money. And considered it a fortune, bragging and grateful, as we talked with the neighbours coming down the path from the Church, calling across in the procession of traps on the road home from Mass, or around the blazing log fire when friends "mitched" in at night for "Spoil Five" or "Nap" before trudging home down stony, pot-holed boreens to unlighted homes, sure-footed as cats in the inky darkness to which we were utterly accustomed.

The death of an old friend during the week, allied to the time of year, is responsible for this dose of nostalgia. The only person in the world who continued calling me "Little Monica" (mother's pet name for her pudgy four-year-old), I felt particularly sad at Martha's passing.

"Charge-hand" in the local grocery-cum-drapery store, Martha, a bright-haired bicycle-riding, camogie-playing, friendly young woman looked after our simple drapery needs – the winceyette night-dresses, the sensible interlock knickers (always blue or pink), the ounces of Mahony's four-ply, for the exquisite torture of learning to turn the heel of a man's sock, and the quarter yard of pink calico for hemming, top-sewing and (tear your hair out again, Nell McCafferty) the Serious Business of making a perfect gusset for the sides of men's shirts.

I walked across the fields to exchange a few words of wholesome chat with an elderly neighbour who cares only about her dog and her cat and her few hens which have the "life of Reilly" scratching away in an old-fashioned farm-yard, exactly as their ancestors did fifty years ago.

The frost on Tuesday night gone, the delicate austerity of the December countryside was beautiful. There is something about the nakedness of a winter's landscape that touches the heart, a subtlety in the sombre tints when the low afternoon sun catches the leafless trees, and the black regiments of dead thistles (disgraceful farming, though that is) added, in some peculiar fashion, to the picture.

Good visibility, as we country people are well aware, is an evil weather portent, the best days being with a soft mist over the hills. December, however, seems constantly to provide heartening exceptions to this rule and, in the transparent purity of the air, far horizons are brought not only into focus but into a delightful familiarity.

First time for ages I could really see the top knot of trees up on Balfe's Hill and, over at the edge of Byrne's pond, I actually spied a heron. Lovely moment, and I was reminded of a glorious day's bird-watching I had enjoyed a few years ago, the ornithologists in the party a marvellous bunch of people, one nicer than another. Why don't we do more of that?

What a wonderful hobby for youngsters. They are not encouraged enough, I'm afraid. And here, I beat my own breast in guilt.

(December 1983)

PLUCKING THE TURKEY

By all the law, the last of our turkeys will have left the premises by midnight on Christmas Eve – which is when Christmas, as I like it, begins. This week is murder, pure and simple, with customers wanting this, that and the other, but then, as Grandfather, the soul of philosophy when he is not actually involved, keeps reminding me: "We would be worse off had we no-one to buy the wretched birds".

At this time of the year, I am afraid that is how I think of them but, come next Spring, I expect I shall step on the treadmill once again, order my poults and start the vicious circle for the umpteenth time.

Odd, in this mechanical age, to find us still killing and plucking in the old-fashioned way. This year, for the first time in ages, we have even saved feathers – my daughters have developed a cushion craze and synthetic filling is too expensive – and all I regret is not having geese.

It would be marvellous to have wings for banisters and hearth cleaning, not to mention goose grease for bronchial complaints and preserving boot leather and horse harness.

How would present-day leather respond to it, I wonder? Interesting speculation, as is the thought of suggesting that a youngster would submit to the indignity of goose grease smeared liberally on chest and back and covered with a large "scapular" of thick brown paper. An unfailing remedy for bronchial colds!

Plucking, in my young days, was a community operation, like the threshing. Neighbours gathered at each other's farms to help, and I remember how difficult it always was to recognise people after a couple of hours at the job, especially when it was geese they were plucking.

It was hard work, but they had to keep going to stay warm because, apart from one small hurricane lamp, there was neither light nor heating.

We carried out the operation in the loft, which was spacious and, having a wooden floor, was supposed to be cosier than outoffices. To this day, if I close my eyes, I can see big burly men coming down the narrow stone stairs, a bird in each hand, feathers sticking out from under battered trilbys and thick moustaches festooned with white down.

Then there was the disgusting job, in my eyes, of washing dirty feet, hundreds of claws, one grimier than the other, and then the serious business of trussing. This was an expert's task, because a well-trussed bird looked so much better and consequently fetched a better price.

I remember getting 2/6 per lb for turkeys and feeling quite pleased. Two shillings and sixpence – twelve and a half pence in today's money! The thought gives me the shivers. Today, turkeys are over sixty pence but, like everything else, inflation has eroded the profit and I bet we brought home more in the old trap with our turkey cheque than we ever shall in the car.

Wasting even a mouthful at the price is sinful and, for those of you who have families who get tired of cold turkey, what abut serving it in a white sauce? The usual white sauce – melt two ounces of margarine or butter, add an ounce of flour, stir well, allow to cool over very low heat, and add a pint of milk slowly, stirring as it thickens. A few spoons of finely chopped onion, some chopped mushroom, pepper and salt of course, and then your chopped turkey which only needs five minutes to cook through. For extra embellishment, a few spoons of cream, a chicken cube and a drop of white wine.

Quite delicious, and it can be varied by being used as a filling in pastry or, if you have lots of time, lining patty cake tins for a hand-around supper.

(December 1976)

CHRISTMAS EVE

The countryside is awash after all the rain, and I could go on about the dreariness of the scene outside the kitchen window.

But it is Christmas and, in spite of the weather and the events of the past week, I must concentrate on cheerful things – like the scarlet of the berries on the holly which the girls have tucked into every conceivable nook and hook, and the comfort of flannelette sheets in bed these nights.

Tucking the sprigs of berried holly into the fretwork front of the old Carr family dresser is one of my favourite Christmas jobs. That same dresser so nearly went the way of many farming antiques during the Thirties and Forties, before we became aware of the value of ancient, well-made sturdy furniture, an easy prey to the dealers who tempted us with a few paltry pounds – but how we needed those same pounds, come to think of it?

Of course, times are hard today. One wonders how we shall survive what is ahead, nuclear fallout, a nine per cent cut in milk production, a ten to twelve pence cut in the intervention price of beef, unemployment rife, pessimism everywhere!

It was worse during the economic war of the Thirties, however. Make no mistake about that, but then people had more iron in their backbones, so we survived.

Youngsters, God help them, are unable to accept deprivation. I know many parents who literally are scared of vexing their children, unable to endure the sulks and bad humours that follow a refusal to attend a disco or stay out late. It bothers me, I must say, to see children over-indulged – and it is happening on every side.

The light of genuine innocence is in the eyes of the twin Murphys, five years old and on tip-toe with excitement waiting for Santa Claus. Nostalgically, I recall a china-faced beauty of a doll I found on the end of my bed one Christmas morning in the Thirties.

Am I dreaming, or were dolls prettier when their faces were china? Such miracles can be achieved with plastic that it seems unlikely, but thinking back on "Penelope" (emphasis mistakenly, of course, on the first syllable) with her pink cheeks, speedwell blue eyes and gentle smiling mouth a little open to show her pretty wide-apart teeth was a delight.

If I had her today, she would be an antique, worth a fortune, but alas the inevitable accident and the china face was smashed to pieces on the flagged floor of the kitchen.

The same floor was the only place we could practice on the roller skates which a city aunt, unaware that we lacked any other smooth surface in that untarred road era, sent on another memorable Christmas. How my unfortunate mother put up with us falling around her as she tried to get dinner is a mystery – and I have the temerity to condemn present-day parents for spoiling!

Happy Christmas to all readers and, if the superstition about it being lucky to see a robin before midday tomorrow, Christmas Day, is true, may you all do just that.

(December 1982)

DECEMBER 31

This last day of the year – the one on which we read and hear a *resumé* of what has been happening during the past 12 months. And we say to each other, "Hasn't this year flown? It doesn't seem a year ago when such and such happened".

Time flies more quickly with advancing years, I feel, although it is re-assuring when the young ones keep saying that the days and months go quickly for them, too. Sad, though, in a way! Youth is so precious – the pity is that the young cannot appreciate this fact.

"Don't keep wishing your life away", my mother used to tell us when we voiced our longings for something in the future. We hardly listened. How could she know how we felt in our vigour and strength? And now, we get the same twinges of rheumatism and it stops me from complaining when I remember how boring it was listening to her (God love her) going on about her aches and pains.

It has been a hard year, inevitably harder for some than for others, but no one escapes the crippling burden of unemployment. How do the politicians cope, I often wonder? Being responsible for ruling the country is such a fearsome thing. Do the "Bosses" sleep at all with the worry of it?

Whatever about that, in farming, we must always look ahead. Certainly, there are lessons to be learnt every year, but there is no point in dwelling on past mistakes or misfortunes. And no future, either, in looking for trouble. "Think positively", say the Yanks. We all know people who reply to your "Isn't it a lovely day?" with "Ah, but it will rain later".

Could it be that they say these things to appease Providence – like spitting over your shoulder when you see a magpie? There can be few businesses so completely in the hands of the weather as farming – unless fishing. We are certainly not complaining this year. To date, it has been a superb winter and we are grateful.

Yesterday morning, incredibly, blackbirds, thrushes and robins were singing. For blackbirds to sing at this time of year is remarkable but, harmonising with the others in this premature dawn chorus, the sound was clear as a bell. My heart lifted and stayed up, which was great.

Premature bird-song is readily explained, of course. It is the first tuning-up of a hymn to the sun, and begins with the realisation that yesterday's daylight lasted that little bit longer than the day before and today's will last longer still. The source of life is reasserting itself and the temporary custodians feel its reinforcement.

Sharing life with all creation, we have every reason for participating in the general revitalisation when the force which has in general ebbed, begins to flow again. Good to be alive this day!

(December 1983)

MESSAGE FROM THE IRISH CANCER SOCIETY

The Irish Cancer Society is deeply honoured to be associated with this very special book.

Monica's "Country Diary" was always a joy to read. Her little vignettes on aspects of country living transported us all from our hard urban environment and awakened childhood memories in those of us who no longer live in the country.

Monica had a special affection for daffodils and the Irish Cancer Society's Daffodil Day. She wrote glowingly about these lovely flowers as symbols of life and hope.

Every March, she would remind readers that the Day was approaching and praise the wonderful work of our daffodil-funded nurses who bring care and support, free of charge, to cancer patients and their families in homes and hospitals throughout Ireland.

The daffodil has become the symbol of the Irish Cancer Society's work to prevent cancer, save lives from cancer and improve life for those with cancer through patient care, education and research.

This hopeful symbol epitomises the progress we are making worldwide in the fight against the disease. Advances are constantly being made in the prevention, diagnosis and treatment of cancer. The Irish Cancer Society works to ensure that these advances are translated into practical help for people with cancer and their families in this country.

This compilation of Monica's evocative country diaries will bring great pleasure to those who have loved her column over the years. It will also help the Irish Cancer Society to provide care and support for people with cancer in communities all over Ireland.

Thank you, Monica.

Dr Desmond Carney
Chairman, Irish Cancer Society